Croft Remote

Croft Remote

by

Tom MacIver

The Pentland Press Limited
Edinburgh · Cambridge · Durham

First published in 1994 by
The Pentland Press Ltd.
1 Hutton Close
South Church
Bishop Auckland
Durham

ISBN 1 85821 135 2

Typeset by Elite Typesetting Techniques, Southampton.
Printed and bound by Antony Rowe Ltd., Chippenham.

Chapter 1

A refreshing breeze of westerly wind rippled the blue waters of the Minch, making them sparkle and scintillate in the bright July sunshine, restoring vitality and movement to a scene which, scarcely an hour before, had been one of torpid listlessness and inactivity. The richly coloured fronds of tangle, breaking the surface of the receding tide and shining like burnished bronze, swayed backwards and forwards, like an army of soldiers with shields held aloft, advancing and receding with the ebb and flow of battle. A heron, fishing for its afternoon meal, stalked the fringe of the tide, one step at a time, and then a pause, like an angler moving down a river bank. A herring-gull, suddenly swooping down to the water's edge, seized an unwary crab and then, soaring aloft, dropped it on the bare rocks. Having thus shattered the hard shell, it now alighted to enjoy the succulent tasty bite at leisure.

At the side of a rockpool, the solitary figure of a small boy sat crouched on his haunches, motionless as a statue, gazing intently at a toy sailing-boat which was bravely tossing its way across its miniature inland sea. Lost in his reverie, he saw himself as another Columbus, braving the dark unknown in search of hidden worlds. Each ripple on the pool was a mountainous wave, each little stone a hidden reef, or perhaps some tropical island which had to be carefully circumnavigated, until at length a sheltered haven would appear where he could rest his weary crew, replenish his dwindling stores of food and water and repair his storm-damaged sails and spars. From time to time he waded out to guide the little vessel off some hidden shoal, or to redirect it when a stronger puff of wind turned it off its course. His bare feet and legs, tanned to a mahogany brown, seemed scarcely to touch the barnacled rocks as he raced from one side of the pool to the other, ready to take command of his ship when it reached the farther shore.

Occasionally the boy's eyes lifted towards the little cottage standing a short distance back from the shoreline. The green sward of rising ground in whose shelter the cottage had been erected formed a perfect background to the dazzling gleam of its whitewashed walls. The thin column of blue peat smoke, which now began to rise and drift away from the stackless chimney-head, told the boy that his mother had built up the fire in preparation for the cooking of the evening meal. But it was not the thought of the approaching meal-hour, or of the appetising smell of hot flour bannocks which would now be spreading through the little cottage, that stirred the boy's interest. From the cottage his eye quickly shifted to the distant ridge of hill which he now eagerly scanned for any movement that would indicate the return of his two older brothers from the 'moss'. Engrossed though he was in his solitary game of make-believe, he still longed for the companionship that would come with the return of his brothers from their arduous toil on the peat moor, spreading the heavy wet slices of peat that fell in a seemingly never-ending flow from their father's peat-knife. Murdo, splashing about in the cool water of the rock-pool, could picture them now, standing in the bottom of the muddy peat-hag, legs and hands and faces smeared and caked an even blackness as they toiled backwards and forwards at their arduous task. Periodically there would be a short respite when they could straighten their aching backs, as their father, starting to cut a fresh row, would throw the peat direct from the 'toruis-sgian', landing each one with unerring accuracy in a neat orderly row, for a distance of seven or eight feet; and then, when the column of glistening black slabs had extended beyond the limit of his throw, the two lads would bend once more to their toil.

Murdo himself would normally have been doing his full share of the back-breaking work along with his brothers, but today he had been kept at home by his mother to 'go a message' for her. This much sought-after duty entailed a journey of three miles on foot to the general store that supplied virtually all the commercial needs of the community. These three miles, however, were a mere nothing to a pair of sturdy bare legs that were used to carrying their owner full twenty miles a day in his scampering round the croft on routine tasks or along the seashore in boyhood games; and there was always keen competition amongst the three boys for the coveted privilege, which today had fallen to Murdo, not particularly because it was his turn to go, but because the two older boys, being stronger, could better supply the labour required for the peat-spreading.

As soon as the hill squad had set out, Mrs Maclean turned to the business of getting Murdo equipped for his expedition. His patched and well-worn trousers were changed for the better pair which he wore at school and on semi-important occasions such as the present one. A neatly darned jersey was donned for the sake of respectability and to conceal his trouser 'galluses'; and, with face washed and hair neatly brushed, he was ready for the journey. A slip of paper in his trouser pocket ensured that he would not forget any of the items which his mother required, and with a snow-white pillowslip rolled up and tucked under his arm for carrying his purchases, he was soon on his way. Now he sped along, as swiftly as any bearer of the Fiery Cross, his brown bare legs spurning the dry and dusty road, his feet apparently impervious to the sharp edges of road-metal that protruded from the sand-bound surface.

Loping along with effortless ease, it took little more than five minutes for the boy to leave behind the last of the line of croft houses that straggled along in an irregular continuity for the first mile of his journey. In all that distance, the curl of smoke that lazily rose from each cottage chimney was almost the only sign of life that showed itself, for every able-bodied person in the township would by this time be on the peatmoss, helping with the cutting and spreading of the winter's supply of fuel while the spell of idyllic weather, so important for the drying of the peat, lasted.

Now on turning the bend of the road, about halfway along the route to the shop, the sparkling water of a small lochan came into Murdo's view. The sight made Murdo's eyes sparkle as brightly as the water itself, and drove his feet to twinkle more speedily, as if it required an increased pace to keep the stretch of water in view. In fact, the existence of the lochan, and a neighbouring one a little further along on the opposite side of the road, joined by a short gurgling burn about three or four feet wide, was by no means the least of the reasons why the trip to the little shop was so eagerly sought after. Both lochs and burn abounded in golden-skinned, red-spotted brown trout, which Murdo and his brothers considered to be fair game for their ingenuity as fishermen, in spite of the many warnings which they had received about an activity which the grown-up folks chose to term 'poaching'. But indeed half the enjoyment of catching trout in these lochs lay in the excitement of knowing that, anywhere in the long heather, there might be a gamekeeper lying, ready to pounce on any marauder of his landlord master's sporting domain.

From the lower end of the loch, at which the boy had now arrived, there flowed a tinkling burn, the loch's outlet to the sea; and here he now left the road, striking through the heather, until he reached a point about a hundred yards downstream. With a quick glance around to ensure that there was no-one in sight, he crawled under an overhanging rock, removed some loose boulders of stone from its base, and drew out an object, the purpose of which would most certainly have puzzled any uninitiated person. Two pieces of hazel branch, one bow-shaped and the other straight, had been lashed together in the form of a letter D, or semicircle, about two feet in diameter. Round the edge of this had been laced a piece of herring net, fully three feet long, tied together at its extremity to form a bag of net, much like an angler's landing-net, but without its handle. Having examined it carefully to ensure that the net was intact, Murdo approached the burn with cautious steps. Selecting a spot where the banks were not much farther apart than the width of his 'caoll', he placed a couple of boulders at each side to make the stream still narrower, and there he wedged his improvised fish-trap, making sure that the straight side was as close to the bottom of the burn as possible. Returning to the rock hiding-place, he now drew out a stout cudgel, also of hazelwood, armed with which he made a wide detour away from the burn, but gradually returning to it about thirty or forty yards upstream. Looking around once more to make sure that he was not being observed, he began prodding and poking in the stream with his cudgel, beneath stones and under the banks, all the time moving quickly downstream towards his fish-trap. The intention obviously was to disturb the burn-trout, and frighten them downstream, where they would be swept into his trap, and held there by the force of water rushing through the narrow neck which he had constructed. But on this occasion he was doomed to disappointment; for it was still too early in the season for any fish to leave the loch and start to search for spawning beds in the running water. All that his net contained was a slimy mass of green weed, which the violent disturbance of the water had dislodged from the bed of the burn. Having cleaned as much of the weed as possible out of the net, Murdo restored both it and the cudgel to their place of concealment, covering them up again with stones, and finally pressing back the long heather that grew around the rock, to ensure that no prying person, such as a gamekeeper, chancing to take shelter under the rock, would notice the unorthodox and, to such a person, quite illegal, fishing implements.

Regaining the roadway Murdo now proceeded at a leisurely pace to recover his breath after his strenuous efforts at the burnside. But when he reached the side of the loch itself, it soon became evident by his furtive movements (had there been anyone present to observe them) that his piscatorial adventures were not yet finished. Once more leaving the road, he made for a point of land jutting out into the loch, again taking what precautions he could against being watched by hostile eyes. From a hollow in the ground, shrouded by a clump of long heather, Murdo drew out a bundle of net, which he proceeded to spread out on the shore of the loch, unravelling any tangled parts and removing twigs of heather which had got enmeshed in it. This was quite evidently a more orthodox type of net than the one which had been used in the burn, although its use would certainly not have found any more favour with the proprietor or his gamekeeper. It, too, was a piece of herring-net, about nine feet long and three feet deep. The top edge had been strengthened with a length of thin rope stitched to the net and to which a row of small cork floats had been fastened. At each end was a length of stout twine and on one of these a stone, roughly oblong in shape and weighing about eight ounces, had been attached. The other cord ended in a loop which Murdo now slipped over his left wrist. Carefully picking up the net by the cork floats one at a time, he set it in folds, which he grasped in his left hand, so that the corks were draped over his wrist, and the depth of the net hung loosely down. Finally he took the length of cord in his right hand, with the stone dangling about eighteen inches. With a final quick look round, Murdo waded into the loch as far as his bare legs would allow him without getting his trousers wet. As a last preliminary to 'shooting' his net, he plunged his left hand into the water and dragged the net along until it was thoroughly wet, in order to make it sink more quickly. Then, swinging the stone backwards and forwards to give it momentum, he cast it out as far as he could; at the same time, with carefully co-ordinated handwork, releasing the cork floats from his left hand so that the net flew out in a graceful spiral until checked by the cord which was fastened to his wrist, and then settled down with the corks bobbing and dancing on the rippling water. One more stage of the operation had still to be carried out. A fairly large stone was now attached to the inshore anchor cord, which was then carefully tautened under water until the corks sank just below the surface, thus concealing them from any casual observer, or indeed from anyone who did not come right down to the waterside. Having completed this to his satisfaction, Murdo then returned to the roadway and continued his journey to the shop, now only one mile and a half distant, or ten minutes if measured in terms of the time which it would take his nimble feet to carry him there.

Sidetracking the main road in order to shorten his journey, Murdo's route took him across the side of a hillock by a narrow footpath which gradually dropped downwards towards sea level. On coming round a spur of rock, his goal now lay before him – a building quite large by comparison with any house in Portandubh, nestling in a little sheltered hollow, a mere stone's throw from the shore. In front and behind it stretched several irregularly shaped fields, each one separately enclosed by its own drystone dyke, or bordered by a fence to divide cornfield from meadowland, and rootcrop from hayfield. A magnificent panorama now unfolded itself to the young lad's vision. Below him the sparkling sunshine danced over the rippling surface of a sea loch which stretched out, first to a group of verdant green islands, the largest of which showed ample signs of active habitation with a ring of crofts circled round a perfect natural harbour, and then to the distant headland of Gairloch, where the hills melted into the summer haze. Leftwards the coastline extended out in a greatly curving line to a point where the loch suddenly disappeared behind a bold headland formed from the massive shoulder of Ben Mor. As far as eye could see, more and more crofts of varying sizes, divided into long, narrow strips of cultivation to facilitate drainage, ran down to the shoreline, each with its little thatched and whitewashed cottage standing midway between the highest and lowest point of cultivation, except for a few, scattered throughout the township, creating a pleasing pattern of irregularity by being situated either higher up or lower down, according as the builder-owner had desired a commanding view from the higher ground or shelter from the winter gales by building on the low-lying reaches of his croft.

After one momentary glance at a scene already quite familiar to him, Murdo's attention now turned to the main purpose of his journey. Even apart from the joy of being released from the gruelling toil on the peatmoss, it was always a delight to visit the little shop, to inhale once again the mysterious multiplicity of smells and odours that pervaded the building, and to enjoy to the full the mouth-watering flavour of the sweetmeat which the generous-hearted shopman, or his equally kindly sister, invariably gave to children, when their purchases were completed.

It was all so awe-inspiring, so breathtaking, to stand there, surrounded by articles of merchandise which had travelled from far corners of the globe, and from places which were geography-book names to the lad. Barrels of Canadian apples; crates of Spanish oranges; sacks of French onions; gammons of Danish bacon slung from the ceiling; huge rounds of Cheddar cheese standing on one end of the counter; pairs of boots that dangled from pegs on the open rafters; piles of gaily-painted floor-brushes; freshly baked bread packed in carefully washed meal-sacks; boxes of butter in bulk, their New Zealand origin branded on their sides; chests of Ceylon tea standing side by side with bags of West Indian sugar; tins of syrup and casks of treacle, and rolls of Kirkcaldy linoleum: all were spread around in a wonderful confusion of multi-coloured display, and each one lent its own peculiar odour to the wholesale pot-pourri that could be found nowhere else than in a country shop.

One corner of the shop was reserved for rolls of drapery piled one on top of the other in a riot of colour, blended from gaily coloured cotton prints, crotal-dyed harris tweeds and floral-patterned cretonnes. Another corner was a hardware store with stacks of pots and pans, carpenters' tools, and gardening implements. The space on the customers' side of the counter, small in dimension as it was, was further reduced by piles of zinc baths, enamelled basins and pails and several heavy coils of Manilla rope of various thicknesses, each roll sewn in canvas and with an end of rope protruding from the centre, inviting a would-be purchaser to uncoil and measure off his required length of rope, fathom by fathom, while the shopkeeper attended to the needs of other customers; and then the length of rope, cut off and coiled into a neat bundle, is silently handed across the counter to be placed on the scales and priced according to its weight. If ever the expression 'from a needle to an anchor' was truly applicable it was here in Cameron's emporium.

Ranged on a shelf immediately behind the counter, making their own contribution to the colourful scene, rows of tall, wide-mouthed 'sweetie'-jars displayed their tempting contents. Black-striped balls, cinnamon balls, ju-jubes and gums, liquorice allsorts and peppermint strongs, paper-wrapped toffees of various brands (always referred to as caramels), pear-drops and pan-drops, golden-coloured candies and red-lettered conversation lozenges – all stood there in a tempting array before the eager, shining eyes of the young customers. Sometimes a housewife from the little township would hail the young shopper from her doorway and would ask him to bring her a 'message' from the shop; and the rewarding coin would procure 'a pennyworth of sweeties', the chosen variety being pointed out with an eager finger. A strip of paper twisted by the shopkeeper round his index and middle fingers formed a pixie-shaped 'poke' and then, with a long-handled scoop, a generous quantity of sweets, far above any imperial measure of weight, would be shovelled into the paper poke and handed over the counter in exchange for the penny.

Today, on arrival at the shop Murdo found the shop door closed; but that was not unexpected. Who, except children, would have free time to go shopping in the morning, especially during a spell of fine weather that demanded the presence of every able-bodied person in some activity of outdoor work? Murdo knew however that a knock on the door of the house adjoining the little shop would summon out the shopkeepers's sister, who would attend to his requirements. So, in next to no time, he was handing across the counter the slip of paper on which his mother had carefully jotted down the required 'messages'. As each item was supplied, the lady behind the counter marked the price on the paper, while Murdo carefully stowed the articles into the pillowslip which served as his homely shopping-bag. The transaction being completed and a polite query about the welfare of his parents being answered, Murdo slung the well-filled bag across his shoulder and was quickly on his homeward way.

One more stop was necessary on the return journey in order to lift the net which he had set. A sweeping glance of his keen eyes round the glen assured him that there was no-one in sight to challenge his 'rape of the loch'. It required only a few seconds to get down to the bank and haul in the net where, to his delight, he found two struggling brown trout firmly enmeshed. A quick rap of their heads against a stone soon ended their struggles and, in less time than it takes to tell it, the net was rolled up and stowed away in its cache, and Murdo was once more on his way, with the two trout stuffed into his trouser pocket with no thought for the fish smell which would linger there, gathering strength with each passing day, until his mother would eventually trace the putrefying odour to its source, and, as so often before, would have to wash the garment out.

By the time he had arrived home it was too late to go and join his father and brothers on the peatmoss, so after changing back into his workaday clothes, he betook himself to the shore, where he and his brothers spent most of their leisure time. And now as he played with his model boat he repeatedly looked, and longed, for the return of his playfellows. At length his patience was rewarded. Over the brow of the hill he spotted the figure of his father steadily descending, head and shoulders thrust forward to counterbalance the creel of peats on his back; and behind him, walking in file, came the two boys in

Chapter 2

Supper-time over, the three boys still lingered at the table. At any other time they would have been asking to be excused from the table long before their elders were finished, so impatient would they be to get out of doors to indulge in their boyish ploys and pastimes. But now they waited in silent expectancy, while their parents finished their meal at leisure and talked over domestic affairs. Their two sisters, aged fourteen and thirteen – both older than the three boys – sat on at the table talking to each other in undertones so that they would not disturb their parents' conversation, while they waited to clear the table and wash the dishes.

At last their father pushed back his chair and rose, feeling in his pocket for his tobacco pouch. The boys rose too, in silent anticipation of what would come next. But they had overlooked two chores which were still to be performed. 'Boys,' said their father, 'have you taken in peats for the evening and fetched fresh water from the well?' Like a flash they dived for the curtain-shielded recess beneath the kitchen window and, each seizing an enamelled pail, they rushed out and headed for the spring, some hundred yards behind the cottage, which supplied the household with all the water required for drinking and cooking purposes. For other general needs, there was a plentiful supply of rainwater, caught in a water-butt as it fell from the roof of the cottage. Hurrying back with the water at a speed which threatened to splash a full third of the contents out of the pails, the boys then carried in armfuls of dry peat until they had filled the wicker basket which stood in a corner near the kitchen fire. Now they again waited, hovering near their father, but not daring to break in on his silent contemplation as he puffed at his pipe; for well they knew from past experience how to interpret his moods. Any rash interruption, any importunate query, breaking in on his after-supper routine, would only serve to ruffle his temper, and in all probability deny themselves the pleasure which they so eagerly longed for. But at last their moment came. Knocking his pipe against the open fireplace to clear out the dottle, their father rose and spoke again: 'Haven't you got your rods ready?' With a united chorus of 'Yes!' they rushed out ahead of their father and, each seizing a bamboo cane about twelve feet long, they headed for the shore where, in a sheltered inlet of the rocky coast, a small but sturdily built rowing-boat lay moored to a rock above high-water mark. By the time their father had come down at a leisurely pace, the boys had unmoored the boat and laid out a succession of three-foot lengths of wood to act as rollers on which the boat would ride over the rough boulders of rounded stone which formed the beach. With Murdo and his father on one side and the two older lads, Sandy and James, on the other, the boat, held on an even keel, slid smoothly over the wooden rollers into the water. The rollers were again collected and placed above reach of the incoming tide, the bamboo rods were placed safely in the stern of the boat, and the boys, scrambling aboard, sat while their father pushed off from the shore.

At a word from their father, Sandy, the oldest boy, took one oar while Calum himself took the other, and thus they guided the boat gently out, propelling it by a thrust of the oar against the rocky sides of the inlet, until they had reached a part wide enough to let them set the oars in the rowlocks and turn the boat with its bow towards the open sea. Calum then took both oars while Sandy, needing no further instruction, took a plank of wood and set it resting on the gunnels, athwart the boat, to serve as an elevated seat from which the three boys, sitting facing the stern, could now more easily operate their fishing rods. The rods were simple, unsophisticated pieces of equipment – a twelve-foot length of bamboo cane to which was attached a length of corded fishing-line, immediately below one of the nodes of the cane, about two feet from the tapered point, and then wound spirally round the cane towards the point, where it was again firmly tied with a couple of double hitches. The line then extended for the full length of the rod and had attached to it a catgut cast with three fishing-flies spaced along it. The flies had been tied by the boys' father, with white seagull feathers whipped to the back of a fish-hook about two inches long. A short piece of red worsted thread completed the simple fly-dressing, but this was all that was necessary to tempt the saithe that abounded along the rocky coast.

For the first half-hour while the sun was still high in the western sky, the boys caught nothing. Motionless they sat, their rod points dipped in the water, while their father rowed the boat at a leisurely pace, about fifty yards offshore. At last, with the sun beginning to dip towards the horizon in a blaze of golden glory, Murdo felt a persistent tug-tug on his rod. Quickly raising his rod point in the air, he played the struggling fish towards the boat. Then, with an upward swing of his arms, he lifted the fish out of the water and, as it swung towards him, he dexterously caught the line and lowered the fish into the boat, where he deftly unhooked it. Leaving it to flap around on the floorboards, he let his flies drop back into the water again. A few moments later it was James's turn to hook a 'cuddy' as medium-sized saithe were called locally, and very soon the three boys were busily engaged in hauling in the green-backed, dark-skinned fish. Sometimes the boys realised from the more vigorous struggles of their catch that two fish had simultaneously seized their flies, and this required more careful playing before lifting the fish clear of the water. Once, Calum had to ship his oars and come to the aid of Murdo whose arms did not have the strength to cope with the struggles of three cuddies fighting on the end of his line. With the rod point raised high to get the full benefit of the rod's flexibility, Calum skilfully allowed the fish to tire themselves out before drawing them to the side of the boat and lifting them in one by one.

But now the sun had set, the light was fading to a soft translucent twilight glow and gradually the 'rise' of fish dropped off. Calum now called on the two older lads to take a spell at the oars, one oar each, to give him an opportunity to fill and light his pipe. Carefully they changed seats, only one person moving at a time, to avoid undue rocking of the little craft, and soon they were underway again, the two boys pulling at the oars, while their father, sitting straddled across the improvised seat, with both rods tucked under his leg, puffed contentedly at his pipe. An occasional fish still rose to the trailing flies, although not so frequently as to present any difficulty to Calum's handling of the two rods.

His smoke finished, Calum again took over the oars, and turned the boat homewards while the boys fished on, eagerly hoping that the fish would rise again. But the light had now faded to something less than twilight – a soft gentle darkness that still revealed the shadow of the shore, outlined against the gleam of the water that still gave some reflection of the cloudless sky. From the oar-blades, as they broke the surface of the water, sparks of phosphorescent light swirled in an iridescent gleam and then faded into the dark water behind the boat.

As they neared the little inlet where the boat was kept, Calum told the boys to tie up their lines, which they did by fixing the end hook in a loop of twine, attached to the rod for this purpose, and then drawing the doubled line downwards to the base of the rod where it was securely tied. Gently the boat was guided shorewards, Sandy again helping his father by taking an oar to steer the boat away from the rocks on the side of the cove. Once ashore, the boat was partially pulled out of the water, then the fish, the oars, and the rods were removed to lighten it. The rollers were once more laid down on the stony beach, and bit by bit the boat was hauled up to its resting place above high-water mark, the crew being assisted in this by Jean and Betty, the boys' two sisters, who had been watching for their return. While Calum secured the boat to its mooring point, the boys gathered up the rollers and other gear, and the fish were filled into a bucket brought down by the girls in anticipation of a catch. Then, stiff with sitting so long cramped up in the little boat, the party wended its way towards the cheerful glow of light shining from the cottage window. Supper was already laid on the table – a welcome sight to the fishermen whose appetites had been keenly sharpened by their activities and by the bracing sea air. After supper the two girls again washed the dishes while the boys gutted and cleaned the fish. Then, at a signal from their father, Jean and Betty fetched him the big family Bible and gave out copies of the New Testament to the rest in preparation for family worship. When all was quiet, Calum selected a psalm and in a deep rich baritone voice started to sing it to the tune

'Kilmarnock', all seven voices joining in. A passage of New Testament scripture was then chosen and read aloud by the five children, each reading a verse in turn. When they had completed the chapter, the bibles were closed, they all knelt with bowed heads over their chairs, and in deep and reverent tones Calum gave thanks to his Creator for guiding them safely through another day, then prayed that He should watch over them during the night.

This simple act of worship being completed, and the bibles stacked neatly away, candles were lit and with 'goodnights' and 'sleep tights' the children all trooped off to their beds leaving their parents to carry out whatever household duties they might still have to perform before they too retired to rest.

Chapter 3

With the peat-cutting completed, Calum Maclean's attention now turned to the equally important task of haymaking, in order to ensure a plentiful supply of winter fodder for the two milking cows which supplied the household not only with milk, but also with butter, cheese and crowdie. The hay-crop was garnered from natural grass growing on those parts of the croft where the soil was not deep enough for other crop cultivation, its growth being encouraged by a liberal layer of farmyard manure, spread over the ground in the spring.

A profusion of wild flowers such as wild white clover, red Dutch clover, purple vetch and yellow buttercups grew in the grass, affording not only a riot of colour through the verdant green, but also adding to the volume and richness of the crop.

Later in the season after the hay had been gathered into the barn, Calum would undertake the cutting of his corn-crop of oats, which was utilised mainly for feeding the lambs during the winter months after they had been weaned from their dams. At this work the assistance of the boys would again be required to follow behind their father, gathering the swathes of corn into bundles, which were then tied into sheaves, using bands made from the straw. Calum himself would attend to the setting up of the stooks of eight or ten sheaves, each stook pointing end on to the direction of the prevailing wind, so that they would not be so liable to get blown down.

Without the crofters being aware of it, their simple methods of harvesting contributed greatly towards a conservation of wild life which was fast disappearing elsewhere from larger units of cultivation where the development of winter sowing, with resultant early ripening, and the introduction of mechanisation, were speeding up the harvesting of crops, thereby destroying the habitat of birds which nested in the hay meadows and cornfields. At Portandubh it was still quite common in the summer evenings to hear the rasping sound of corncrakes all around the crofts. Many times the boys tried to trace the source of the call, in the hope of catching a glimpse of the elusive bird, but never once were they successful.

It was all very different with regard to the sighting of the cuckoo when it arrived in late April. Not only could its double-note call be heard on most mornings in May, but it was quite a common sight to see it flitting around, or even to spot it perched on a fence-post. The aspiring young bird-watchers were greatly puzzled over a poem which they had learned at school and which spoke of the cuckoo as 'a wandering voice', a term which they considered could be much more aptly applied to the corncrake, a sighting of which had always eluded them.

Wielding the scythe was not a task which any of the boys could safely undertake, especially as the scythe blade had to be whetted repeatedly, a manipulation which required much skill, so the lads were free to indulge in their pastime games on the seashore, sailing their home-made model boats, or bathing and swimming.

The pool where they sailed on 'voyages of discovery' with their little vessels was tidal, washed each day by the incoming tide, but left still and unruffled when the tide receded. About a hundred feet long and three feet deep, it was a safe and ideal place not only for sailing their boats, but also for bathing and swimming. Here the boys spent many hours in summer, often stripped of all clothing, so that their entire bodies became tanned by sun and wind as brown as any Red Indian, while the soles of their feet, so accustomed to their scampering over the rocks, developed a skin the toughness of leather. Indeed, from early May until the end of October their feet were never enclosed in the 'prison cells of pride'. But as wintry conditions grew nearer, lowering temperatures aroused parental insistence that hobnailed boots, the regular winter footwear of all boys, must once again be donned. But these were faraway days yet, so they could still enjoy to the full their barefooted freedom of movement. And here, at the so-styled bathing-pool, they indulged in their games of make-believe. R.M. Ballantyne's Coral Island, a large boulder about ten feet long, lying at one end of the pool, once more became the refuge of shipwrecked Jack Martin, Ralph Rover and Peterkin Gay. The good ship *Hispianola* again sailed to Stevenson's *Treasure Island* to discover the pirates' ill-gotten gold, which took the form of a collection of empty sea shells, tucked away in a little hollow on the rock. Sir Thomas Lipton achieved in make-believe a success which his *Shamrock* had five times failed to do in reality, and sailed home in triumph with the 'America Cup' although to any casual and unimaginative observer the 'cup' would have looked suspiciously like a battered sewing thimble. Blennies lurking under stones at the shallow end of the pool became transformed into ferocious man-eating sharks which threatened the survival of the intrepid swimmers, who had been diving in search of sunken treasure round the wrecks of ships that had foundered on the coral reef. But invariably the swimmers succeeded in reaching shore and safety just as the cruel jaws were about to snap on them. A skin-graze on their bare legs was certainly not caused by having slipped on the barnacled rock, but was clear proof of how close they had come to being caught by the monster.

But now the advancing tide was beginning to lap the edge of the sloping rock which contained the water in the pool. It was an unwritten rule that the pool must be abandoned for safety reasons as soon as the tide began to flow into it. There had been a previous occasion when the ignoring of this rule had resulted in a period of suspension from all forms of seashore recreation, so the three boys were careful never to commit another infringement which might result in their being denied their pleasures. The boats were carefully stowed away in the 'boat-house' under an overhanging rock, safely beyond the reach of even the highest spring tide. Their scanty summer garments being merely a shirt and a pair of knee-length trousers, it took them only moments to get dressed and then make their way back to the cottage, where the usual daily chores which were their responsibility had still to be performed – carrying in peats from the peat-shed and fetching buckets of fresh water from the well.

When the evening meal was over and 'grace after meat' had been said, the boys waited expectantly for any mention of another fishing trip. But when their father, rising stiffly from the table, mentioned a sore back, aching with his daylong swinging of the scythe in the hayfield, the lads sensed that there would be no launching of the boat that evening, so they betook themselves off to a part of the croft which was too stony for cultivation or even for haymaking. With home-made 'camans', or clubs, cut in a nearby hazel wood, and a herring-net cork which had outlived its original usefulness, they now engaged in a sort of three-cornered style of shinty game, where each player vied with the other two for possession of the ball. Time meant nothing to the three combatants and the game would possibly have continued non-stop till daybreak had their elder sister not come out in the darkening to summon them in for family worship and bed.

Chapter 4

The days that followed were not all just fun and play for the three lads. The peats, which had been cut and spread out to dry a fortnight before, would now require to be 'lifted' to expose their undersides to sun and wind. The system followed was to set one peat standing on its longer edge, then stand two more leaning against it at each side, standing on their shorter end, and a sixth peat was placed flat on top with its wet side facing upwards to the sun. This was back-breaking work as it entailed continuous bending until the entire cutting had been set up in heaps of six; and of all the tasks on the peatmoss, this was the one that everybody disliked. But at length it was finished, and they could all now turn to the much more genial toil of hay-making.

The swathes of hay, still lying on the croft where it had been cut, now had to be turned over in order that the underside would dry, so an array of home-made, wooden-toothed hay-rakes was brought out. While Calum made for the potato field to undertake the much more difficult and onerous work of weeding and earthing up the drills of potatoes, the five children tackled the work of turning and shaking out the sweet-smelling hay. An added bonus to this quite pleasant task was the prospect of coming on the 'byke' of a colony of bumble bees, built into the foggage so close to the ground that it had not been disturbed by the swinging scythe. Now the bees, roused by the probing teeth of the rake, betrayed the location of their hard-earned stores, and the boys, eager to get at the rich-smelling, sweet-tasting honey, immediately snatched the honeycomb away, seemingly impervious to the fierce attacks of the defending bees which, in the words of Rabbie Burns,

'. . . Bizzed oot wi' angry fyke
when plundering herds assailed their byke'.

No doubt Burns himself had experienced both the pleasures and the pains of such a situation when helping his father in the hayfields of Mount Oliphant during his boyhood days.

Later on the hay would be raked into heaps, ready for Calum to shake into rounded 'coils', intended to resist the penetration of any rain that might fall before it was gathered in. Gathering in the hay was the most enjoyable work of all, tiring though it undoubtedly was. On a bright sunny morning the coils of hay were again shaken out to get rid of any dampness that might still be lingering in them. Then, each young labourer taking a doubled length of rope, a bundle of hay was made, in size according to each one's physical strength; the rope was fastened round the bundle with a running noose; any straggling wisps were carefully dressed off to avoid spillage and loss on the way and then, each helping the other to get the bundle hoisted on their shoulders, they all trooped off to the barn where their loads were unloosed at the barn door, and back they went for another load until the hay was all gathered in.

Then came the part of the operation to which they most looked forward. While their father carefully forked the hay in with a pitch-fork to one end of the barn, the children trampled it down. As the pile grew higher, with the attendant possibility of someone falling off, so the excitement increased, until their father decided that the younger members must now come down, the excuse being offered that there was no room for everybody. A short ladder was placed against the eight-foot high pile and Murdo, being the youngest, came down first, followed by James and then Sandy, leaving the two girls to complete the job – ostensibly because they were the oldest and heaviest, but more likely because they were not as prone to larking as the boys. By this time they had to move cautiously as their heads were now in close proximity to the rafters of the barn.

At length the last wisps of hay were trampled into place and the girls descended, ready like the rest of them for the supper which would now be awaiting them.

Next day, Calum announced at breakfast that the peats would now be ready for stacking. This was always done on the peatmoss, each stack being built on the site of the previous year's one, the seasoned peats having by this time been brought home and stored in the spacious peat-shed. Over the years the dross crumbling from successive stacks had built up a gentle mound, ideal for drawing off any rain that would fall on the stack throughout the winter months.

Peat stacking was an activity in which virtually every able-bodied person assisted. Indeed, quite often the only people left at home in the township would be the aged and infirm, even children in arms being taken, cradled contentedly in a shawl, and laid down in the shelter of some heather knoll while their mothers lent a hand gathering the dry peats.

A well-known Gaelic song, which has an English version, tells of a mother who left her baby lying sleeping while she went, not peat-gathering, but harvesting, and the child was carried away by the fairies. Although she searched far and wide, seeking the help of both bird and beast, she never found the baby again. However, no such sadly mysterious happening ever occurred at the Portandubh peat-stacking, and any babies brought to the moor slept undisturbed in the sweet-scented air, laden with the honeyed aroma from the surrounding clumps of heather.

Mrs Maclean's first and most important duty of the morning, after breakfast and the daily morning session of family worship, was the equipping of the peat-gatherers for their midday alfresco lunch on the moor. As it would have meant much wasted time and effort to make the trip down to the cottage for a meal, and then back up again for the afternoon's work, a lunch-basket was prepared, with bannocks of oatcake thickly spread with rich home-made butter, and layered with slices of cheese, also home-made, although not from the same milking. While the butter had been churned scarcely twenty-four hours earlier, the cheese had been made a full twelve months before, pressed for several days to remove every drop of whey, and then hung up in butter muslin to dry and mature. Now its rich flavour acquired partly from its twelve-months' maturity and partly from the caraway seeds liberally sprinkled through it, would both whet and satisfy appetites that had already been keenly sharpened by open-air toil.

Beside the oatcakes went a package of golden, puffed-up, floury girdle scones which would literally melt away in one's mouth, even without the layer of luscious home-made blackcurrant jam or bramble jelly, which could be spread on them from the jar carefully tucked into a corner of the basket. Or else it might be a rich and thickly-fruited slab of cold 'clootie' dumpling, cooked the night before. This delicacy, Mrs Maclean's speciality, was always the sign of some very important occasion, perhaps a Christmas or New Year's Day dinner (when it was served piping hot, with the added cause for eager anticipation of the hope of finding the lucky threepenny-bit, wrapped in greaseproof paper, and carefully concealed in the steaming dish). Equally important, although less festive, were these periodic trips to the peatmoss for the cutting, lifting and stacking of the peats when the dumpling was of course served cold. At all times, the preparation entailed a great deal of work. No household bowl being large enough to contain the amount of mixture required for a family of seven, the biggest basin from the milk-house was appropriated for the purpose. Minute pieces of suet were thoroughly mixed with a monumental heap of sifted flour-meal, then vigorously stirred into a stiff batter, sweetened with sugar, treacle and a great quantity of large blue raisins; the mass was then tied up in a piece of white cloth, carefully greased and floured to prevent the water, in which it was boiled, penetrating into the mixture. The only receptacle large enough to hold this and allow for expansion was the family washpot which, thoroughly scoured out, was elevated to the rank of cooking-pot; slung from the 'crook' over the kitchen fire, it contentedly bubbled and gurgled round the sleek, swelling sides of the dumpling, carefully watched to ensure it did not boil dry. When finally dished the cloth was opened up to let the dumpling cool, in readiness for the morning. To complete the provision of the alfresco meal, a tin pail was filled with rich refreshing buttermilk, the residue of the previous day's churning, for the freely perspiring peat-gatherers always found their task a thirsty one.

It was imperative that the peats should be gathered together and stacked as soon as they were dry enough, in case the weather broke, bringing the heavy rain that so often came in July and August. Not only was it important to get the peats into the stacks thoroughly dry, but also, if heavy rain came, the ground underfoot would not withstand the continual trampling of feet as the peats were being brought to the location of the stack, and it would quickly become a soggy quagmire.

The work was, of necessity, a concerted effort requiring many hands and in some cases, where household numbers were small, two or more families co-operated to carry out the work; but in the case of the Maclean family there were enough hands to form a complete team and get all their own peats stacked before they too went to give neighbourly assistance to elderly people who did not have young folks of their own to help them.

Various modes of transport were used for the work – a wheelbarrow, precariously guided up and down a six-inch wide plank, which formed a temporary bridge across the peat-bank; a handbarrow, which was in effect a four-handled stretcher, requiring two people to carry it with its load of peats; a peat-creel; and for the younger children canvas sacks which, in their better days, had contained bolls of oatmeal. At first all members carried the peats to the site where the stack was to be built, dumping them in a heap about ten feet long. Then Calum began to set the peats in an orderly way, gradually building the pile to a height of about seven feet, while the rest of the workers emptied their loads to form a ring round the embryo stack within reach of Calum's hand as he moved round the stack. Next, a wall of peat was built round and against the stack, each peat being laid in orderly fashion, end outwards and overlapping each other in such a way that any rain falling on the stack would run and drip off it without penetrating this outer layer. Finally, a row of heathery turf was set along the top to prevent any seepage of rain through the stack.

While Calum was completing one stack, the rest of the family moved on to the next peat-bank to start the process all over again; and so the work progressed until ample fuel for the year ahead had been secured.

A welcome break in the day's toil was the midday meal, when weary limbs were stretched on a dry, heather-scented hummock, healthy appetites did full justice to the delicacies of the picnic basket, and thirsts were slaked with draughts of rich buttermilk. Round about them the soothing hum of bumble-bees gathering their own rich harvest from the vast stretches of ling heather lent an air of gentle peacefulness to the scene.

Chapter 5

Portandubh Bay was not actually an inlet enclosed by two extending arms of the mainland, as one might expect from the name. The southern shore of the bay – or sea loch as it really was – was formed by two islands, Eilean Risteal and Mulagrach, the two most northerly of the Summer Isles. Between Risteal and the mainland stretched a narrow channel about a quarter of a mile wide which could be crossed dryfoot during the ebb of spring tides, but which was deep enough for the local fishing-boats to negotiate when the tide flowed. Eilean Risteal was about two and a half miles long and a half-mile channel of deep water separated it from Mulagrach, which was a mile and a half in length. The shelter afforded by this four-mile extent of the two islands made the bay a safe place for boating and fishing in clement weather. But the bay faced westwards, open to the Minch, and when westerly gales came blowing straight in, the waves lashed the rock-bound shores in fearsome fury, and no small boat could have survived in them. Such storms did not occur frequently, but could be expected at the time of the equinoxes. The crofters and fishermen, whose lives as well as their livelihood depended on their knowledge of weather conditions, could generally read the signs foretelling a storm and make preparations in an attempt to minimise any possible damage. Small boats were hauled high up the beach and roped down if in an exposed position. Even the larger boats, which were generally left at anchor, were moved to more sheltered places in the lee of the island shore. Round the crofts cattle were brought home and milked early so that byres could be closed up before the storm broke. Sheep seemed able to sense the approaching storm and flocked to take shelter behind stone dykes and rocks, or even in the lee of the cottages and outhouses. Stocks of water and peat were hurriedly replenished to obviate the need for anyone to venture outside.

By the time that all precautionary measures had been completed the sun, moving towards the western horizon, was passing through lowering clouds with a dull, lurid glow, far removed from the glorious sunsets of summer. While the water still maintained a sullen calmness, as if Nature was trying to deceive and trap any unwary creatures still riding the seas by springing a surprise on them, large flocks of seabirds – eider ducks, cormorants, guillemots and razor-bills – came crowding in to find shelter in the bay.

At length, from as far as the eye could see out over the Minch, fitful gusts of wind came stealing furtively over the surface of the water in a dark forbidding frown, then another and still another, each one coming at ever-lessening intervals, until the waters of the bay were lashed into white-capped waves that came racing and tumbling on to the shore as the fury of the gale rose higher and higher.

Now the voice of the storm-king began to be heard by the families gathered round their blazing peat-fires, at first a low moaning sound like some lost soul wailing in mental anguish. Gradually the moaning increased to a shrill whistle that rapidly rose to a crescendo of shrieking madness. The sea now became lashed up into a maelstrom of boiling waters that hurled themselves onto the rocks as if resenting the obstruction that they caused. Waves were sent towering high in the air where they were again caught by the wind, now at near hurricane force, and carried along like a driving rainstorm, lashing the windows of the Macleans' cottage with such persistence that it became impossible to see through them.

Farther out in the bay, the surface water was being swept up in clouds of spume that were then blown along like smoke from a forest fire, swirling and writhing towards the shore.

Inside the Macleans' house, the noise of the wind booming in the chimney-head sounded like the thundering roar of cannon, and intermittently there came gusts which caused the very house to tremble. But, built low as it was for the very purpose of withstanding such winds of hurricane force as were now being experienced, and with solid stone walls fully four feet thick, it had withstood many such storms before, and the inmates did not feel they had any cause to worry.

Darkness fell early and was intensified by the heavy storm clouds that hung low in the sky. While Mrs Maclean and her two daughters prepared the evening meal, Calum and the three boys sat around the blazing peat-fire and whiled away the evening with a card game of 'Catch the Ten'. Then, with supper and the evening family worship over, the entire family retired early to rest.

By morning the fury of the storm had abated as the wind gradually blew itself out, but seas were still running high and there was considerable turbulence along the shore where heavy billows rolling landwards still made it unsafe for anyone to venture too near. The three boys would have dearly liked to go beachcombing for there was almost certain to be jetsam carried in by such a fierce storm and there was always keen rivalry amongst all the boys of the township to see who would get to it first. But beachcombing was strictly forbidden until conditions had further ameliorated, so the lads had to content themselves with accompanying their father round the croft, surveying for any possible storm damage. Some thatch had been blown off one corner of the byre roof and that would mean a trip to the hill to cut some heather; for that was the material used for thatching the outhouses. A short section of a fence had also been flattened, where three fence-posts had snapped at ground level. Repairing this would be a first priority to ensure that the livestock did not get in and damage the crops. As it was fairly common occurrence to get fences damaged, either by storms or by attempted inroads of cattle, Calum always kept a reserve supply of fence-posts at hand, so this repair was carried out immediately, and life, which had been only slightly disrupted by the storm, quickly settled back into a routine pattern.

Chapter 6

Halfway along the shore of Eilean Risteal facing the mainland there was a lovely stretch of golden sands, an ideal spot for having picnics and for bathing, although, of course, not easily accessible except by boat. But the lack of a boat with a responsible adult available to take charge was no deterrent to the Maclean children when they were free from any household duties and they wished to have a picnic. It was no problem for them to walk along the shore around the head of the bay, a half-hour's journey to the channel that separated the island from the mainland.

There were several factors which had to be taken into consideration and satisfied to determine the accomplishing of such an expedition. First of all it had to be a Saturday when they were not attending school, unless it was summer holiday time. Then they had to get parental approval to be released from home and croft chores and also to get supplied with the all-important picnic basket. The weather had to be favourable for such an outing, which had also to coincide with the spring tide, calculated by the new moon or the full moon, so that the crossing could be accomplished on foot during the ebb tide. But most important of all for the first such expedition of the year it had to be early in the month of May, for reasons which will be explained later. So, with all these conditions requiring to be satisfied simultaneously, it will be readily understood that such outings were quite rare occurrences, and were therefore looked upon as red-letter days.

But let us assume that the sun did shine, bright and warm, on a Saturday morning early in May, just at the time of the new moon.

Equipped with their picnic baskets, hastily prepared that morning, and adequately supplied to meet appetites that would be keenly whetted by the fresh air and the exertions of the journey, the five youngsters set out. Allowing themselves ample time to reach the point where they could ford the channel, they did not even wait until they could cross dry foot. In order to give themselves as much time as possible on the island, they waded into the water as soon as the tide had ebbed sufficiently to permit them to do so. Moving in single file, with Sandy leading, to find the shallowest part, they edged their way across until they reached a point where the water was clearly getting shallower. As soon as they had all reached dry land, the three boys went racing and scampering across a mile-long stretch of low-lying, heather-clad ground, until they arrived at the sandy beach. They immediately stripped off their clothes and, with much splashing, went racing into the sparkling water lapping on the beach, with complete disregard for the fact that the temperature of the sea, so early in the year, was anything but warm.

Meanwhile Jean and Betty, coming along at a more sedate and leisurely pace, now arrived at the beach and headed for a level grassy area, bordering on the sand, and often used on previous occasions as their picnic 'table'. It did not require two calls to bring the boys out of the water to share in the picnic repast which their sisters had laid out on a snow-white kitchen cloth spread on the grassy sward; and very soon five healthy appetites were doing full justice to the wholesome fare which their mother had packed for them.

The meal over, the reason for the boys' eagerness to have an outing at this particular time of year was now made apparent. A few hundred yards beyond the sand, a low spit of rock and shingle ran outwards to the sea, and it too became a separate island when the tide was in. Here large numbers of seabirds nested every year and their eggs were considered by the local people, especially the younger folks, to be a great delicacy. Herring-gulls, common gulls, black-headed gulls all nested on this headland which, being low-lying, was easily accessible. Many of the birds, particularly the herring-gulls, simply laid their eggs in some depression of the rock, without any lining of grass or other material. Others scooped out shallow hollows in the sand or shingle, and again, without any attempt at lining it, they laid their eggs there. But the green-grey shells of the eggs, speckled with brown spots, camouflaged them so successfully that the boys had to step very gingerly to avoid the possibility of tramping on the nests.

It was important to gather the eggs early in the nesting season, before the parent birds had begun to sit on the clutch. Mrs Maclean who was very knowledgeable in a wide range of Natural History and well-versed in the nesting habits of the sea birds, laid down certain hard and fast rules about the way the egg collection must be made. Only one egg should be taken from a nest, and nests which contained more than two eggs must not be touched as there was a likelihood that the parent bird would now be sitting on the eggs, since three was the number usually laid. There was no guarantee, however, that these rules were not occasionally 'bent' a little. The boys had no orderly, systematic method of carrying out their search, so it was quite possible that after one of them had removed an egg from a nest containing two, another of the boys might come on the nest and remove the remaining egg in all good faith, thinking it was a 'first'. But there was no real danger of over-depleting the nests. The means of carrying home the eggs being limited, the boys could not take much more than two dozen with any degree of safety and as the number of eggs in the area could be counted in hundreds, and since birds that had just started to lay would continue to produce a full clutch unless their nests were excessively depleted, no serious harm was done to the colony.

All the time that the search was going on, the parent birds wheeled and swirled overhead in a screeching cloud, protesting loudly against this intrusion of their domain, and at times swooping low over the heads of the boys as they raided the nests. This was particularly so with a small colony of terns that were also nesting there. Although the boys were not interested in the terns' eggs, which were much smaller than those that they were seeking, the elegant and graceful sea-swallows, as they were often called, dived so close to the intruders that the boys could feel the swirl of wind from their wings, and hear the clicking noise they made as they tried to drive the intruders away.

No doubt members of the Society for the Protection of Birds, had it existed then, would have protested loudly against what they would declare to be a threat to the survival of these species, but it must be remembered that it was all part of a way of life which had always been accepted by the crofting communities, and they were always careful not to deplete the bird colonies to a point which might endanger their survival. Indeed, in some parts of the Highlands survival of these colonies shared importance with their sheep stock.

While the youths were egg-collecting, Jean and Betty cleared up the remnants of the picnic and repacked the baskets. Then, with the boys safely out of sight, they modestly retired behind some rocks on the seashore and donned their bathing costumes but, on stepping gingerly into the water, they found it so cold that they made only a token attempt at taking a dip and then they quickly dressed again.

While all this activity was going on, acting on a strict warning from their parents, a watchful eye was kept on the tide, and when it was noted that the ebb had ceased, the girls knew that it was now time to make for the crossing to the mainland, before they were cut off by the advancing tide. The boys were summoned from their egg-collecting, the picnic baskets were retrieved, and the return journey accomplished, just as the tide was beginning to lap over the ridge of shingle that constituted the fording place.

Supper for the boys that night was seagulls' eggs, hard-boiled, which to them was a great treat, though their parents and even their two sisters were not quite as epicurean in their tastes, and satisfied themselves with the usual home-baked bannocks and cheese.

Chapter 7

Apart from the routine activities of crofting life, such as peat cutting, potato planting and similar duties which extended over several days and had continuity of engagement, there were certain important household tasks that cropped up each year and were generally of one-day duration.

This was an age that was decades before the introduction of mechanical appliances for the performing and lightening of housekeeping chores, even in urban areas, and it was inevitable that such chores placed a heavy physical burden on womenfolk, especially in communities where the houses did not have even the simplest of house services such as piped water. The washing of family clothing, normally done once a week (weather permitting), demanded the drawing of large quantities of water from sources that were often quite distant from the houses. The only existing 'washing-machine' was the housewife herself, and the only appliance available to her apart from her own two hands, was a scrubbing-board, a wooden frame holding a corrugated sheet of galvanised iron, which she placed in her wash-tub, and on which she rubbed the clothes up and down to bring them to the spotless cleanliness that amazingly she succeeded in achieving.

In later years, long after these boards had been discarded in favour of suction plungers and other more modern appliances, scrubbing-boards were again resurrected, not this time for their original purpose, but for the ingenious use of youthful musicians in skiffle-group bands, who produced a sort of percussion-type music with these and other improvised instruments.

In summertime the wash-tub was generally placed outside the house, sitting either on two chairs or on a bench improvised for the purpose, at a height that enabled the work to be carried out without excessive back-bending. But in winter or inclement weather the small kitchen, which also served as the living-room, lacking in any form of ventilation other than the rather tiny window, became clouded in steam from the washtub and from the washing-pot bubbling on the peat fire, to such a degree that the occupants of the room could scarcely discern each other's features, and the male members of the household were glad to escape outside with an excuse of some outdoor task irrespective of the weather.

But in addition to the weekly washing-day, there was another important event which generally occupied one day of the year – the annual blanket-washing. Some time during the months of May or June, the halcyon period of Highland west coast weather, careful observation was taken of the weather signs to ensure that, as far as was humanly possible, a day could be chosen that promised to be dry and sunny for this highly important performance. As far as the Maclean family were concerned, the day chosen was preferably on a Saturday in order that the children could lend a hand.

Close to a little burn that tinkled its meandering way through the croft land, Calum had built a rough-and-ready fireplace with blocks of stone, sufficiently firm and stable to support the huge washing-pot, which as already described served several housekeeping purposes. With a peat fire burning cheerily under it, and with water filled from the nearby burn, the pot would provide the large quantities of hot water required for an operation that would take up a major part of the day.

Blankets were now stripped from the various bedrooms, and brought out to the open-air 'wash-house' where the family washtub now stood ready in close proximity to the fire. The tub was a home-made utensil, one of two which Calum had made from a disused fifty-gallon paraffin cask acquired from the local general merchant. By cutting the cask in two across the middle and then cutting two handgrip openings at opposite sides of each half-cask, the result was a pair of very serviceable tubs, one of which, in addition to being used as a washtub, was also taken into the house each weekend to be utilised as the family bathtub.

While the water in the wash-pot was coming to the boil, a blanket was placed in the tub along with a generous helping of 'soft soap', a commodity which was purchased in seven-pound tins; for this was long before the days of the modern washing-powder packets that now vie with one another boastfully on television advertisements. The tub was then topped up with hot water, if necessary reduced to a bearable temperature with cold water from the burn. This was the moment for which the three boys had been impatiently waiting. It was their share of the work, a duty which they greatly enjoyed, to get into the tub with their bare feet and trample the blanket in the hot soapy water. From time to time they had to step out of the tub so that their mother or their sisters could turn the blanket over and then they stepped back to continue the process – a primitive forerunner of the modern washing-machine. Only two of the lads could find room in the tub at one time, so it became the third lad's task to keep topping up the wash-pot from the burn, when hot water had been withdrawn from it. But each boy had to take his turn at this in rotation so that they all could enjoy their share of the more congenial work of trampling the blankets.

When Mrs Maclean considered that the blanket was now quite clean, she and the two girls wrung the soapy water out of it, each taking an end and twisting the blanket rope-fashion. Meanwhile, the second tub which was standing close by had been filled up with tepid water, into which the blanket was now transferred and thoroughly rinsed in order to remove all traces of the soapsuds which clung to it. It was then again wrung out after which it was carefully carried some distance away and spread out on the grassy sward to dry under the direct rays of the sun.

As soon as the first blanket had been transferred to the second tub, another was immersed in the hot soapy water and amid shouts of glee and not a little horseplay, which at times threatened to topple the young 'launderers' out of the tub, the trampling process recommenced, thereby sustaining continuity of activity from tub to tub and thence to the bleaching-green.

As each blanket dried out to Mrs Maclean's complete satisfaction it was carefully folded and carried back to the cottage, gently permeated with the perfume of the grasses and meadow flowers on which it had been spread, and smelling soothingly fresh with its cleanliness.

Chapter 8

Throughout autumn, winter and spring, from September to April (in fact during all the months with an R in them – the popular but not too accurate way of determining at what time of year shellfish could be eaten) several of the Portandubh crofters turned from agricultural pursuits to supplementing their livelihood by fishing for lobsters, for there was a big demand for this delicacy in city fish markets.

The creels used for trapping the lobsters were of home-made construction, made by the crofters themselves. A base measuring approximately twenty-four inches by fifteen was built with straps of wood and four stout rods of willow or hazel, bent to form a semicircle, were fixed securely to the longer sides of the base. Netting of strong cord was woven on to this frame and fitted with two entrances one on each side and made in a circular shape about three inches in diameter from thick fence wire. These were fixed in such a way that the lobster could enter the trap but could not get out. A heavy flat-shaped stone was securely tied to the base inside the creel, which was also fitted with a cord to which a piece of fish could be attached as bait. To complete the creel a length of rope was tied to one corner so that the creel could be lowered to the sea floor. The end of the rope had cork floats secured to it so that the creel could be discovered when it was time to lift it. Each crewman had a 'drift' of from twelve to twenty creels.

As the lobsters lurked under rocks and in crevices quite near the rocky shore, where there often was a heavy swell from the backwash of the waves dashing on the rocks, there was considerable danger of boats being capsized or swamped, so the lobster boats were sturdily built, with a good broad beam to withstand the roll of the waves. But even so, accidents and tragedies did sometimes happen, casting a deep gloom over the little township, where everybody knew one another and friendship prevailed throughout the entire community.

Generally three men composed a crew, two to man the oars while the third man set, or hauled in, the creels. These were dropped in the water about fifty yards offshore, the rope being long enough to permit the corks to float on the surface, even at high tide. Weather permitting, the creels were lifted each day, and then reset a little farther along the coast so that a fresh area was worked at each setting.

One part of the netting covering the creel could be quickly unlaced sufficiently wide to allow any lobsters caught to be removed from the creel and if necessary to insert a fresh piece of bait. It was then laced up again ready for resetting.

When all the creels had been lifted and reset, the boat made the return journey, either propelled by the oars or by a dipping lugsail if the wind was favourable. For both of these operations two men were required as one man had to steer and to hold the sheet rope, while another had to be ready to operate the sail halyards. Meanwhile, the third man was busy tying the claws of the lobsters, not merely to prevent them from gripping their captors' hands with their powerful nippers but more particularly to prevent them from fighting with each other in the floating cage where they would be kept until ready for sending to the fish market. If allowed to fight unchecked, they would tear each other's claws off, thereby seriously lessening their market value.

About a mile from the end of the township was a little land-locked natural harbour, well-sheltered from every direction of wind. Here, each crew had a floating cage, well-anchored in tidal water that never ebbed completely dry. The lobsters were stored there for they had to be kept alive to be of any value when they reached the market. When the crew had caught a number sufficient to fill a box, specially constructed to withstand rough handling on the long journey south, the lobsters were packed in this box early in the morning and hurried off to catch the mail car which left from Polbuie post office very early. At Broomton the box was transferred to another mail car which took it thirty-two miles to the railway station. There it was loaded on the train for transportation to Billingsgate in London. Undoubtedly some of the lobsters would not survive the long journey which would take well over twenty-four hours, but the fishermen had no means of knowing whether the London salesmen did not exaggerate the number of dead lobsters to their own advantage. Certainly no crofter-fisherman ever grew rich on the meagre cheque which was invariably returned to them but which was just large enough to keep them from being discouraged to such an extent as to make them give up fishing for a commodity which was to the city dweller a very highly prized delicacy.

Weather permitting the creels were set and lifted five times a week from Monday to Saturday; but they were never reset on Saturdays for, to these simple-minded rural dwellers, Sabbath observance was paramount, both as a day of rest and as a day for worship. It was only on very rare occasions that the fiercest of gale-force conditions ever prevented them from taking the creels ashore for the weekend. This presented the Maclean boys with the opportunity for one of the highlights of their pleasure-seeking during the winter months, when it was too cold to indulge in their summer pastimes.

It was not only lobsters that entered the creels and got trapped, but edible crabs as well. The price given for crabs as compared with their weight did not make it an economic proposition to send them to Billingsgate as the transport costs would far exceed the price fetched, so, during the week, the crabs were removed from the creels and returned to the sea. But on Saturdays the fishermen did not wait to empty them until they had come ashore. The boys kept a sharp lookout for the first sight of a returning boat and, with parental permission, they set off to meet the boats as they arrived at a slipway in the little harbour where they stacked their creels on shore and got their catch of lobsters ready for placing in the floating cages. The boys were then permitted to take out the crabs, a task which had to be performed with extreme care as the crabs had pincered claws which were equally as strong as those of the lobsters. Woe betide the unfortunate person whose hand got caught by them. It was very rare for any of the fishermen themselves to take any crabs home or even for their children to come for them, as they did not seem to realise that this was a delicacy in many ways superior to lobster.

With the crabs safely deposited in a sack, which they had brought for the purpose, the boys hurried home with their precious load. They emptied the crabs into their mother's wooden washtub, but had to stand watch over it, as the crabs made stout efforts to clamber on each other's back and claw their way out of the tub. Meanwhile their mother busily cleaned out the multi-purpose washing-pot, which was always taken into culinary service for cooking anything bulky such as clootie dumplings or crabs.

No doubt the Animal Rights Society members had they existed then would have howled in impotent rage if they had been there to see kettles of boiling water being poured over the unfortunate crustaceans, for crabs, like lobsters, cannot be used if they have died before the actual cooking process has commenced. But the boiling water despatches them very speedily and is really the most humane way of dealing with them.

Twenty minutes was the time allowed for the crabs to be properly cooked and then, scarcely allowing sufficient time for the shells to get cool enough to be handled, hammers were wielded to break the claws and remove the succulent white flesh. The bodies were then prised apart to get at the rich layer of meat in the back of the crab.

Under directions from their mother, Jean and Betty prepared the extracted meat, adding breadcrumbs and spices, and served up the mixture in the shells which had been carefully washed.

The boys would have much preferred to have a crab allocated to them so that they could attack it and eat the meat as they extracted it, a method which they had often secretly practised when, on finding a crab hiding under seaweed fronds during a low ebb, they had lit a fire on the shore and cooked the crab in a syrup tin or in a pan smuggled out of the kitchen, although this method, using cold water, was certainly not as humane as their mother's cooking. But their mother knew only too well from experience of former such occasions what a mess they would make, both of themselves and of their surroundings, if given this liberty, so they had to curb their impatience and wait until everything was ready for the whole family to sit at table and enjoy what was looked upon by all of them as a special treat.

Chapter 9

Sunday, always referred to by all devout Presbyterians as 'the Sabbath', was regularly observed, in Portandubh as in all Highland communities of that time, as a day of rest and a day of worship, in strict accordance with Biblical decree. Only necessary works, such as milking the cows and driving them to pasture, and the feeding of other domestic animals, was ever undertaken. A supply of water sufficient to last throughout the weekend was drawn from the spring on Saturday evening and stored in a large galvanised container. Baskets of peat were brought in from the peat-shed. Potatoes were washed and vegetables for the Sunday pot of broth were prepared so that the minimum of kitchen work would be required. Boots and shoes were carefully cleaned and polished. Finally, just before retiring to rest, the menfolk shaved in readiness for going to church next morning.

The church, which served a number of townships, was purposely situated fairly centrally, but it was about five miles from the Macleans' cottage. During wet and stormy weather and especially in winter it was too far for even the older children to walk that distance. When they did go during the summer, custom required that they should be 'decently clad'. Although it was considered quite proper to go barefooted to school, no parents would dream of letting their children attend a church service without donning their 'Sunday clothes' and this included stockings and shoes or boots.

Although during weekdays the children, barefooted, could run the five miles to the post office or shop without tiring, they dared not run on the Sabbath, and in any case with heavy boots on they did not feel much like doing so. The journey was thus too tiring for the younger members of the family.

Occasionally the minister made arrangements to visit and to hold services at one or other of the outlying parts of his parish on a Sunday afternoon. When he came to Portandubh all members of the family were able to attend the service which was held in the schoolroom, this being officially recognised as a meeting-room for religious services, an arrangement that dated from the time of the Education Act for Scotland.

After the Disruption of 1853 when the Free Church broke away from the Church of Scotland over the dispute about Patronage, efforts were made by both churches, but in the Western Highlands more particularly by the Free Church, to build schools and schoolhouses in as many localities as possible, and to supply teachers there. Money was provided by the Church for purchasing building materials, sites were negotiated with the landowners, and the labour was generally provided free by the able-bodied men of the communities to be served by the schools. Such provision of educational facilities had been planned three hundred years earlier by John Knox in his *First Book of Discipline* at the time of the Reformation in Scotland, as he wished to have free education provided for all children throughout the land; but it took centuries rather than years to have this ideal completely fulfilled, particularly in the remote Highland glens which were inaccessible in John Knox's day and for a long time afterwards; so the opportunity for free education for all did not reach Portandubh until the rivalry of the divided factions of the Scottish Presbyterian Church brought it about in order to advance their own religious ideologies.

When the Education Act (Scotland) of 1872 made primary education compulsory for all children of five years and over, the church schools were taken over by locally elected School Boards of Management, but a clause was inserted into the agreement stating that the schoolrooms must remain available for religious services when required, outwith normal school hours, and both the School Boards and their successors, the elected County Education Authorities, observed the condition faithfully.

Although none of the weekday pastimes were permitted on Sunday, the Macleans often took their children for a quiet walk if the weather was fine; but, before setting off, strict injunctions were always given that there must be no running or noisy shouting.

Mrs Maclean who, before her marriage, had been a schoolteacher, was well versed in Botany and Zoology, the elements of which she was expected to teach her pupils, and by gently reminding her children that the wild flowers which grew in such profusion on and around their croft, and the many birds that were to be seen there and along the seashore, were all the handiwork of the Great Creator, she was able to teach them the names of all the birds and flowers that they saw during their Sunday walks without any semblance of guilt that she might be committing the sin of secular teaching on the Lord's Day.

Portandubh appeared to be on the direct line of flight of many migratory birds, and in late Autumn it was a common sight to see large flocks of birds winging their way to warmer lands, or, as in the case of such species as fieldfares and redwings, arriving in Scotland from Eastern European countries.

It was on the occasion of one of the above mentioned Sunday walks that Murdo caused un-Sabbath-like hilarity when he was overheard to remark, more to himself than to the other members of the family, that a flock of birds which had just passed overhead 'were just like a funeral running'. It was indeed not an entirely inapt description, as funeral corteges at Portandubh moved as an irregularly massed cluster of dark-coated men following behind the coffin, which was carried from the house of mourning until quite out of sight, the mourners taking it in turns, four at a time, to man the bier. But the procession's slow and deliberate pace was in direct contrast to the swift flight of the migratory birds, and much to Murdo's embarrassment and confusion, the idea of a funeral cortege running caused a wave of laughter which even his parents were forced to join.

So days that could otherwise have felt wearisome and tedious to youngsters whose energetic animal spirits were curbed by the restraints of Sabbath observance were now brightened by a new interest that was further enhanced by a closer association with their parents than what they sometimes experienced on weekdays when the parents were engaged in the toils of the day and the children were often left to their own devices.

It was during bad weather that the parents were presented with the biggest problem in finding means of preventing the proverbial 'devil finding mischief still for idle hands to do'. Reading of so-called 'worldly books', a term which covered most fictional works, was not permitted, the only exception being books which might be classified as 'morality' books. Playing of table games such as ludo or snakes and ladders was also forbidden. But there did exist two different sources of reading material which provided Sunday reading. Amongst the newspapers which came by post to Portandubh and which were shared by a group of households passing their paper from neighbour to neighbour, there was a weekly magazine called *The Christian Herald*. As it arrived at the Macleans' house on Saturdays, it was much in demand at weekends. As its name indicates, its writings and stories supposedly dealt with moral values, although it must be admitted that there were many instances when these values were rather heavily veiled. But a lenient view was taken of this by the Maclean parents and *The Christian Herald* was duly acceptable as suitable Sunday reading.

The other source of suitable literature was the school library. Early in the century J.B. Coats of Paisley, who had amassed a huge fortune from the making of reels of cotton sewing thread, made his name even more widely known and respected in the Highlands than did the circular labels stuck on the ends of the reels, by distributing gifts to schools throughout Scotland. His first gift was huge blocks of chocolate which could be chopped down to provide hot drinks for children, many of whom travelled three to five miles on foot to county schools, and who had no means of getting a hot meal from early morning till they reached home again at night.

Another gift was a sturdy schoolbag for every pupil, with an ample supply to provide for others enrolling in later sessions. The girls received bags with a carrying handle, in the style of the modern attaché case; those for the boys had two shoulder-straps and were carried on their backs.

But the most widely acclaimed of all the Coats' gifts was a library for every school, a solidly constructed bookcase with glass doors, and a large selection of books to fill its shelves. It was from this source that the Maclean boys had made acquaintance with the heroes of adventure stories written by authors such as Fennimore Cooper, Captain Marryat, and R.M. Ballantyne. But the works of Dickens, Scott, the Brontes and many other well-known authors were also included, for the library was intended not merely for school use but to serve the literary needs of the adult section of the community as well.

Amongst this profusion of fictional literature not considered suitable for Sabbath reading, there was a small selection of books which a broad-minded reviewer could pass as being on a par with *The Christian Herald* and these were accepted by the Maclean ménage and served to lessen the tedium of Sundays, which had to be spent indoors, even although as time went on they were reread many times over. One that was very popular with all members of the family was the story of a little boy in an orphanage entitled *Nobody Loves Me.* Is it possible that somewhere a copy of that old paperback survived to eventually come into the hands of a well-known modern singer, inspiring him to compose and sing 'I'm Nobody's Child'?

Chapter 10

In August with the peats all dried and stacked and the hay-crop nearly all secured, Calum Maclean and the neighbouring crofters now turned their attention to preparations for the herring fishing, that most important activity in the provision of the winter's supply of salt herring, which was one of the chief items of their staple diet. Earlier in the season, when there were any signs that shoals of herring had arrived on the coast, a few nets were set to procure a supply of fresh herring, but these earlier catches were not considered to be of suitable quality for curing.

Now, however, it was time to catch the winter's store and a sharp lookout was kept for the infallible evidence of the presence of herring shoals – the diving solan geese (the local name for gannets) and the occasional appearance of a whale following the shoals – not, as was sometimes thought, in pursuit of the herring, but to feed on the plankton on which the herring were also fattening themselves.

Word was quickly passed round the whole township as soon as the first signs of the shoals were seen. Now the whole place bustled with activity. At every cottage where there was an able-bodied man fit to take his place in a boat, nets were lowered from barn rafters where they had hung for almost nine months, safe from marauding mice that might otherwise nibble their way right through the bundle to make their winter nests.

A first priority was to spread out the nets on the ground and examine them carefully for any broken meshes that might have passed unnoticed the previous autumn when repairs were carried out at the end of the season's fishing. Buoys and anchor ropes were then closely inspected and if necessary the floats were given greater buoyancy by filling them with air blown from lusty lungs.

The nets were again rolled up, tied in bundles, and carried down to the shore where they were carefully laid in folds in the boats ready for 'shooting'.

The first net had a buoy and anchor rope attached to it, and as each succeeding net was joined to the preceding one another buoy was attached. At the same time small oblong stones picked from the beach were tied at intervals to the foot-rope to act as sinkers which would keep the nets upright in the water and prevent them from being swept upwards by the thrust of the tide. When all the nets were aboard, a second anchor rope and buoy were attached, and everything was ready.

Long experience had taught the older men that the likely movement of the shoal would be according to the state of the tide. On rare occasions the herring had been known to come right in to Portandubh Bay, but generally the tide carried them behind Eilean Risteal as the plankton were being swept up into Lochbroom.

As the sun was setting and when the solan geese were again seen repeatedly diving and gorging themselves on their catches, each boat began to set its drift of nets, keeping a reasonable distance apart from each other. Soon the area was dotted with the black buoys bobbing on the rippling waves, and when the last net-anchor was dropped, the boats rowed back to shore to await the coming of daylight, when the heavy task of hauling in the nets would commence.

Murdo and his two brothers always accompanied their father down to the shore to help with the gathering of the sinker stones and to watch the preparations for departure. They would have dearly loved to have gone too, but with the boats heavily loaded with nets there was certainly no room for supernumerary members of the crew. As it was, if the boat was fortunate enough to make a big catch of several crans it would be loaded right down to the gunwales and great care was needed to avoid it being swamped. Many years earlier such a tragedy did occur and only one member of the crew who was a strong swimmer succeeded in reaching the shore.

The boys were however able to share in the excitement of the home-coming. Early in the morning and long before their usual rising time, they were out of bed and mixing for themselves a bowl of oatmeal brose, being too impatient to wait for the pan of porridge which their mother usually cooked for their breakfast. Then, with a flour scone liberally spread with jam in their hands, they sped off as fast as they could to join the boys who were now appearing from neighbouring crofts, all eager to watch for the returning boats.

Watching the flocks of seagulls hovering and swooping over the boats as they came into sight, it was easy to tell which boats had good catches. Much banter, and not a little boasting, went on amongst the boys claiming that their parents' boats had better catches than the others, and sly taunts were thrown at those lads whose boats did not appear to be heavily laden, or to have the attention of many seagulls, sometimes resulting in retaliation with fisticuffs. But the arrival of the first boat ashore put a stop to this as the boys crowded round to see the catch and admire the gleaming mass of silver in the bottom of the boat.

Now all was stir and activity. The herring were scooped into large two-handled willow baskets for carrying home, but first of all small bundles of about a dozen herring were strung on a short length of wire and the boys directed to 'take a fry' to houses that had no menfolk at the fishing. This was simply a neighbourly gesture and none of the fishermen would dream of putting a price on the fish handed out in this way. Not only so, but where the catch proved greater than the requirements of the crew for their own use, the surplus was also passed on to these families, or to boats which had been less successful. But the latter boats would also try again that evening, for the shoals of herring might stay within reach for several days until they finally moved too far down the coast to be followed by small boats, and they would now be pursued by crews from more distant townships.

This, however, did not end the bustle and action. Back at the cottage, while Calum was busy preparing a brine of coarse salt and water which was tested for the right strength by seeing if an egg would float in it, Sandy and James began gutting the herring. The gut had to be removed without splitting the fish open, and this was done by cutting away with a sharp knife a small part of the fish adjoining the gills. In this way the gut was easily removed while retaining the roe or the milt, one or other of which was present in most of the herring at this time of year.

Murdo's share of the work was to carry the gutted herring in a basket to his father, who now began to pack them, belly upwards and as close together as possible, in a wooden barrel, which was made specially for this purpose. After each completed layer he added some of the prepared brine, ensuring that all the herring got impregnated with it.

When the barrel was full it was covered and left standing in the barn for several days. The brine was then poured off and the herring repacked in another barrel, this time being sprinkled layer by layer with coarse salt, but with no water added. A lid was then tapped on to the barrel which was left standing in order that the herring would assimilate the full strength of the salt. Cured in this way they would keep for a long time, and certainly throughout the winter when they would gradually be used up.

Calum Maclean always cured two barrels for his family's use for salt herring was a very important item in the diet of the crofting communities, where butcher meat was a luxury to be enjoyed not more than once a week. For a family the size of the Macleans, one barrel of herring would not give the head of the house a real sense of security.

The traditional method of fishing for herring had always been with the use of drift-nets with the fish becoming enmeshed in them by the gills. The meshes were of a standard size which would hold only mature herring which were the ideal size for curing. Smaller fish of lower quality could pass unharmed through the drift-net meshes. In later years, particularly after the Second World War, it became standard practice to use ring-nets which surrounded a shoal and dragged in fish of all sizes and of varying quality. Stocks became depleted to such a degree that quota catches had to be introduced to prevent the species from disappearing altogether. A further harm caused by ring-net fishing is that the fish, being crushed and squeezed together in the bag of the ring-net, get most of their scales rubbed off which affects their quality when cured.

With the herring fishing season over for the year, Calum turned his attention to repairing any damage done to the nets. Dogfish often followed the shoals of herring, preying on them. Fish enmeshed in a net were an easy target for these predators and, when tearing the herring out of the nets, they often broke the meshes, which now needed to be repaired. This was done by the use of an ingeniously devised tool which all net-makers used, and which Calum himself had carved with patient care out of a thin strip of wood. Most of the crofters were skilled in the craft of net-making, and made their own nets during the long winter evenings as they sat at their firesides.

When the nets were all repaired they then had to be waterproofed to prevent them from rotting. This was a communal activity carried out down at the shore in a sheltered corner of the bay where a rough sort of jetty had been built with huge boulders of rock, and where the boats were hauled up to be secure from winter storms.

Choosing a dry day, a huge iron pot, the joint property of all the crofting fishermen of the township, was set over a makeshift fireplace constructed of large flat stones. The pot was filled with water from a nearby burn, and a fire was lit under it, stoked with peat and with the driftwood strewn along the shore, the gathering of which was delegated to the boys, who never failed to be present at this, or any other occasion which was a departure from the 'even tenor of their way'.

A dark brown substance known as cutch was added to the pot of water, and this was allowed to boil just like a gigantic brewing of tea. Cutch was obtained from the dried bark of a Far-Eastern tree, and was regularly used by the fishermen for waterproofing nets and sails, thus giving the sails the dark brown colour which was so distinctive a feature of the fishing fleets of that time.

When the 'brew' was considered to be sufficiently strong the fire was dowsed and the liquid left to cool. As soon as tough, leather-skinned hands could bear the heat, the nets were quickly passed through the liquid, then wrung out and spread on the surrounding rocks to dry.

It required several fillings of the pot to carry out the operation on all the nets. When the first batch to be treated had dried, they were carefully folded into bundles and tied with stout cord, ready to be stored away for winter, and this made room for the next batch of nets to be spread out. Nobody left the scene until all the nets had been treated, dried and rolled up. Once the work was completed the pot was emptied, turned upside-down and covered with a piece of sail-cloth to protect it from the weather. Finally, using various methods of transport, some bearing the nets on their shoulders, and others wheeling them on sideless barrows specially constructed for the purpose, the nets were taken home and slung to the rafters of barns.

Chapter 11

In this modern day and age one often hears the word 'ceilidh' used with reference to a sort of informal concert, particularly if the programme includes at least some Gaelic songs or traditional Highland folk music. The compere who announces the various items is called the 'fear-an-tighe' – the 'man of the house'. Such functions are most certainly very enjoyable, especially if the instruments being played do not have their musical tones overwhelmed by a cacophony of dreadful noises emanating from a welter of amplifying instruments that look for all the world like the embodiment of a Heath Robinson cartoon, and whose only purpose of existence appears to be to emit deafening and discordant noises that completely drown the sweetness of the melody being played. Fortunately the bagpipes by the very form of their construction have so far defied any possible attempt to connect them to such amplifying mechanisms.

No organised concert entertainments were held at Portandubh and indeed there was no place where they could have been held for the use of the school classroom, the only public building in the township, would have required the temporary removal of the heavy five-seater combined desks and seats which stood on heavy cast-iron legs and were fixed to the floor with long screw-nails. On the rare occasions when there was a wedding in the community, the removal of the seats was carried out by the young men of the township, to allow ample space for dancing their eightsome reels, quadrilles and lancers at the celebrations which always followed the marriage ceremony and wedding feast. But these were the only occasions of organised jollification.

There was, however, many a ceilidh during the long winter evenings. The word ceilidh in Gaelic simply means a visit, and can include the implied meaning of a chat or pastime conversation. When the lengthened hours of darkness brought to an end all outdoor work except those necessary duties such as milking and feeding the cows which had to be done by the fitful gleam of a storm-lantern, time would have hung heavily on isolated little Highland townships did they not have some means of relieving the boredom of enforced idleness. Even those who were interested in reading and who had access to a supply of reading material found difficulty in reading for long by the poor light of a paraffin lamp. Over the years the custom had developed, chiefly among the menfolk, of going 'air ceilidh' – on a visit – to one or other of the neighbouring croft-houses. Some houses acquired a greater popularity than others, depending, perhaps, on the ages of the inmates and also on their sociability and readiness to receive company.

General conversation would develop with an exchange of news on any occurrences in and around the community. A certain topic of conversation would be the weather, so great an influence did it exert on their lives and livelihood; the week's catch of lobsters and whitefish; the price of lambs at the recent sales; the sex and colour of the most recently delivered calf – all were subjects demanding comment.

When the week's news was exhausted and conversation began to flag, the master of the house – the 'fear-an-tighe' – would suggest that some member of the company known to have musical talent would play a tune. With an affected air of reluctance the person named would produce a mouth-organ from a capacious pocket, or the fear-an-tighe might ask his wife to fetch the fiddle or melodeon. Then, with tobacco-pipes filled and lit, the company would sit back and enjoy the Gaelic airs being tunefully produced. This might be followed by a request from the fear-an-tighe for a Gaelic song if he knew that anyone of those present was a good singer. It was considered a discourtesy not to accede to any request, although the man of the house in turn would be careful not to embarrass anybody whom he knew could not perform.

In the Macleans' house, where a celidih often materialised, Calum himself, a good singer and an accomplished melodeon player, was always ready to contribute towards the evening's entertainment. Storytelling was an accepted part of the ceilidh programme on occasions when there was someone present who was known to possess the 'seannachie' talent for this traditional custom, whereby unwritten tales of Celtic mythology or of deeds of prowess by clan warriors of bygone days were handed down by word of mouth from generation to generation.

So the long winter evenings slipped quickly and pleasantly by in a manner that encouraged and strengthened much greater social friendships than are experienced nowadays under the stultifying influences of radio and television.

Weddings, as already mentioned, provided another but very different form of entertainment. It was traditional that the engagement of a young couple must first be celebrated with the holding of a 'reiteach' or betrothal, when the relatives and the closest friends of the bride and groom were invited to the bride's home by her father, who would consider it a blot on his honour not to provide food and drink sufficient to ensure that the evening developed into a night of jollification and merriment.

The prospective bridegroom did not attend for the earlier part of the traditional ceremony. Instead, he was represented by the person chosen to be his best man. Food and drink were first handed round the assembled company until everyone had partaken to a plentiful sufficiency. A relative of the absent groom now called the company to attention for a matter of some importance. The best man stepped forward and announced that he was there to represent the interests of his friend whom he named. With veiled allusions which usually carried a double meaning that caused much laughter in the company, he said that his friend, in a search for good quality livestock, wished to obtain a young mare, sound in limb, of good appearance, able and willing for hard and heavy work, not fiery or skittish in nature, and not yet in foal. As each of the required attributes was stated, particularly the final one, there were loud gusts of laughter from the menfolk while the women, with a show of modesty, affected to be properly shocked at the innuendoes. Finally the girl's father was asked if he could supply an animal with these qualities. Keeping up the pretence of animal purchase, the reply came that he had one or two mares which he could recommend. Jokingly he brought forward a spinster relative of middle-age and stated that here was a mare that had proved herself capable of hard work, although he did not believe she had ever been saddled for riding. This having been received with great roars of laughter, the best man stated that, although she looked to be a fine sturdy animal, her age was against her. After some more banter the prospective bride was finally brought forward, affecting to be very shy and unwilling but she was quickly accepted as being eminently suitable.

By this time the young man who was 'seeking a mare' was summoned from a nearby house where he was waiting and obviously fortifying himself with numerous 'drams' from a hip-flask. He was now brought in to join the company and immediately became the target for some sly bantering jokes and even for a certain amount of friendly horseplay. Toasts were again proposed and drunk, food was again passed round, and as the evening's fun continued with more music and singing of Gaelic songs, the happy couple were now considered to be officially betrothed.

Several weeks or even months might elapse before the actual wedding would take place. It was taken for granted that the whole township would join in the wedding celebrations although no formal invitations were sent out. In addition to the usual giving of wedding presents, the bride's parents were showered with promises of food and drink to provide for the feasting which was liable to continue for several days until the impending approach of the Sabbath brought an end to the festivities.

By the time that the great day dawned, everything was in readiness. Generally the date was made to coincide with the school holidays in order that there was a place available for the dancing which always took place on such an occasion. The fixed schoolroom desks were all unscrewed from the floor and stacked outside. The place was then refurnished with chairs brought from neighbouring houses and also with planks of wood set on makeshift supports around the walls. Here the wedding guests – which meant every person able to walk there – assembled to await the arrival, first of the minister, followed by the bridegroom and best man, and finally by the bride and her bridesmaid. It was quite unknown for marriage ceremonies to be solemnised in the church and if the schoolroom was not available, the marriage vows were taken in the bride's parents' house.

With the nuptial knot securely tied, the bridal party led the company outside, the happy couple being showered with handfuls of rice, which was probably easier to obtain than confetti, perhaps even cheaper, and certainly much easier to sweep up afterwards. And whatever grains might escape the brush would most certainly be pecked up by the schoolteacher's hens.

Every housewife in the township spent the day prior to the wedding baking girdle scones, oatcakes and other eatables in preparation for the feasting that would follow the wedding for several days, not only at the bride's home, which could accommodate only a fraction of the company, but in several neighbouring houses as well. Fowls which had had their necks 'thrawn' a day earlier, were now plucked and boiled in large pots of Scotch broth in readiness for the wedding feast.

With the marriage ceremony and preliminary expressions of good wishes over, the company, headed by the bride and 'groom, walked in procession to the home of the bride's parents where a plentiful supply of drinks had been laid in so that the guests could toast the happy pair with whisky for the men and port wine for the ladies. It was unheard of for a woman to take anything stronger than port and seldom if ever did they accept a second one even of that. Not so with the menfolk who had made ample provision for augmenting the parental supply.

After the health-drinking ritual had been duly observed, all those who could not squeeze in with the bridal party moved off to neighbouring houses to share in the feasting and merriment that now ensued, the fun and joking getting further inspiration by the replenishing of glasses from the bottles of whisky that now circled freely round. There was much singing of Gaelic songs and playing of accordions and fiddles, so that the whole township rang with the sounds of jollification. From time to time, the newly-married couple moved around from one house to another to show their appreciation of all who had assembled to share in their happy day.

As the day wore on into evening, the younger folks, and indeed anyone else who had a mind to do so, started to make their way towards the schoolroom, which had now been cleared of chairs, these having been required back in the houses; but the improvised bench seats still remained.

Soon the skirl of the bagpipes could be heard, intermingled with loud 'hoochs' as the newly-married pair led off the Grand March. This was followed by an eightsome reel, which traditionally always started off an evening's programme of dancing. Gradually the crowd increased to numbers beyond what the floor space could accommodate. Windows were now thrown open to allow the strains of music to reach the sets of dancers who were now beginning to form up outside. Eightsome reels, foursome reels, quadrilles and lancers followed one another in rapid succession, with Highland schottisches, hesitation waltzes, Boston two-steps and military two-steps to add variety to the 'square dance' pattern. With such strenuous activity it was little wonder that the sampling of the bottled refreshment became more and more frequent. Sheer fatigue coupled with some alcoholic unsteadiness would ultimately bring a temporary cessation to the dancing and carousing but even when weddings took place in mid-week, the celebrations and the feasting continued day after day, and only the approach of midnight on Saturday and the fear of desecrating the Sabbath would bring the proceedings to a close and allow the newly-weds to settle down to married life without any thought of a 'going-away' or a honeymoon.

Chapter 12

The year was nineteen fourteen. Newspapers came to Portandubh by post only every second day, such being the isolation of the little township, and half a dozen other neighbouring ones, where mail was received only three times a week. But although all through the summer of that year the newspapers carried rumours of war-clouds gathering over Europe, this did little to disturb the peaceful quiet of Portandubh, except that the young men of the locality, most of whom were volunteers in the Territorial Army, were having to spend more of their evenings cycling five miles or more to the drill hall in Polbuie, to be trained in military manoeuvres and in the use of rifle and bayonet. For it was the ambition of every young lad to join the 'Terriers' as soon as he reached the age of eighteen; and indeed one or two of them succeeded in bluffing their way to recruitment before attaining that age. Not all of them enlisted in the Terriers however, as some of them were keen on the sea and joined the Royal Naval Reserves.

Even when news finally came that war had been declared against Germany because she had invaded Belgium, it all seemed very remote to the minds of young people like Murdo; but not to those families whose husbands and fathers and sons now marched away, fully equipped in their Seaforth Highlanders' uniform and carrying haversacks slung across their shoulders, but this time marching on foot and not, as before, riding on their bicycles, because this time they would not be returning from the assembly point at the drill hall where they were to meet the conveyances that would bear them away to war.

The Naval Reserve volunteers had been called away a few days earlier to report at various naval bases for posting to their ships.

To seven-year-old Murdo the news of war conveyed little significance although as time went on all three boys began to find that less time was afforded them for play as their parents made more frequent calls on them to go to the aid of one or other of the widows of the township whose sons had gone off to the war, leaving her with nobody to carry her peats from the hill, or to fetch her weekly requirements from the shop. But, in the main, the boys did not object to the extra work imposed on them. Having the healthy appetites of boys who spend so much of their time in the open air, they always welcomed the generous 'piece' with which they were invariably rewarded – either a girdle scone liberally spread with butter and jam, or a large slice of oatcake and crowdie.

Young Murdo was an avid reader. Two of his favourite authors were R.M. Ballantyne and Fennimore Cooper, who had both written such thrilling tales for boys. But he also took a great delight in stories from history – books such as Hume Brown's *History of Scotland* and Barbour's *Tales of Wallace and Bruce*. He rejoiced over the Scottish victories at Stirling Bridge, Bannockburn and Otterburn; his blood boiled in anger as he read of the brutal deeds perpetrated by order of the cruel English tyrant, Edward the First, who had put William Wallace to death in such barbarous fashion, and tears ran down his cheeks – just as they had done, as he had read in Aytoun's *Lays*, on the cheeks of Sir Randolph Murray when he brought to the citizens of Edinburgh the news of the disaster at Flodden. Now this new faraway war was pictured in his young mind as just another such occasion, and no doubt he would eventually hear of another great battle fought and won by the men whom he had seen marching away.

Certainly there were changes and innovations relating to the new wartime conditions. As time went on, ration books were issued by the Government for each member of the family, and each time anyone went to the shop, the ration books had to be taken there and little coupons were cut out of them whenever commodities such as sugar, tea and bacon were purchased. There were also coupons for butter and cheese, but these were seldom bought in a shop as they were produced at home when milk and cream were in plentiful supply. Sweets too were rationed, but the few pence that could be afforded for that luxury used up only a small portion of the weekly allocation.

When the little one-teacher school assembled for the new session towards the end of August, the teacher, Miss Mackenzie, showed her pupils a specimen of sphagnum moss, which grew in great abundance on the moors. The moss was required in great quantities for dressing the soldiers' wounds, as it contained certain healing properties. She asked the pupils to gather as much of it as they could and bring it to school.

There were two classrooms in the school for at one time the numbers attending had been much greater and Portandubh was then a two-teacher school, but now numbers had dwindled and only one teacher was required. The moss was shaken out to dry on newspapers spread over the floor of the empty room.

In any school where the teacher had to cope with a wide age range (from five to fourteen), it was inevitable that some age groups would have to work by themselves on assignments such as essay writing or arithmetic, while the teacher took another group for some other subject. In normal times this sometimes afforded an opportunity for dodgers to caper and to play tricks on their more industrious classmates, and even to slyly copy the answer which others had worked out and written down for their arithmetic problems. But woe betide the delinquents if they were spotted by the teacher, who always seemed capable of keeping one eye roving over the whole classroom while guiding and encouraging the group which was receiving direct tuition from her.

Now, however, the teacher had a new inducement to offer the pupils in order to make them work assiduously at whatever assignment was set them. The prospect of going through to the empty classroom to work at the sphagnum moss became an incentive to all the children to get their work finished quickly and correctly. They could then go and start picking out bits of grass and other foreign bodies to make it fit for use in the military hospitals where it would be sent. The clean moss was packed in sacks, Red Cross labels were attached to them, and they were transported by the mail car and then by train to their destination. But to the children the attraction of this work lay in their getting out of the main classroom, away from the restraining eye and word of authority of their teacher, and away also from the humdrum routine of 'lessons', the general term applied to all classroom work.

The men of Portandubh and the neighbouring townships who had joined the Territorial Army, formed one company of a battalion of the Seaforth Highlanders regiment, and that regiment, in turn, became part of the Fifty-first, or Highland, Division. After mobilisation the division was quartered at Bedford where they spent the autumn and winter months getting intensive training on army manoeuvres and rifle drill. In spring small detachments of men began to get home on leave prior to embarkation to France. While at Bedford many of the soldiers who, in their isolated communities, had never been exposed to the germs of infectious diseases such as measles and scarlet fever, succumbed to these illnesses. When they came home on leave, often much too soon after contracting such troubles, the germs came with them, and very soon an epidemic raged. It spread so rapidly and proved so virulent that Miss Mackenzie got permission from the Education Authority to close the school. Even if she had kept it open, she would have had no pupils attending, so wide was the spread of the trouble, and so widespread the fear of an illness previously outwith their experience and which now tragically caused the deaths of two of the school pupils.

Naturally the enforced holiday was a great delight to all the pupils, including the Maclean family, but, in spite of being kept in isolation from any known contacts, all five children were laid low with measles, although Murdo remained apparently immune until after his brothers and sisters had recovered when he too succumbed, thereby earning the approbation of his schoolmates for thus extending the period of the unexpected holiday.

When eventually the epidemic had burned itself out and the health authority, in the person of the 'Sanitary Man', had ensured that all infected buildings and homes were thoroughly disinfected by the burning of a sulphur candle set alight on a shovel or other receptacle in every room, life then returned to normal and the school reassembled after a three-month break.

Chapter 13

On Saturdays, when free from any of the normal chores and when no extra duties were required of them, Murdo and his two brothers took great delight in beachcombing along the inlets of the rocky shore, searching for flotsam or jetsam carried there by the strong tides and prevailing winds of the Minch. On one occasion after a westerly storm they spotted a large tree-trunk which had probably been part of a deck-cargo of timber being shipped in from Norway; large quantities of timber were now required by the shipyards. No doubt the deck-cargo had been washed overboard during the storm, or else lost from some cargo vessel sunk by enemy action. In fact it transpired that quite a quantity of timber was washed ashore along the coast, where it was too inaccessible for the Receiver of Wrecks to make it worthwhile claiming as Government property. To the crofters it was real treasure-trove as the logs could be cut into serviceable lengths for use as fence strainers.

The three boys succeeded in securing a rope round one end of the log and then they anchored it as high up the shore as the advancing tide would carry it. Then, when the tide had receded, they laboriously levered it above high-water mark and went home to report their successes. Some time later to their great surprise a crofter came along to speak to their father and to offer to buy the log for one pound. As Calum had no particular use for it, his fences being all in good order, the bargain was clinched, much to the delight of the boys, who each received six shillings and eightpence from the sale. This was untold wealth to the lads, who had never before possessed more than sixpence at any one time. It so happened that, shortly before this, their teacher had started a National Savings Branch in the school, encouraging the pupils to start saving their pennies and to buy savings stamps 'for the war effort'. Each stamp cost sixpence and was affixed to a card bearing the pupil's name. When a card held thirty stamps the teacher took it to the local Post Office and a savings certificate was issued in a little green book with the pupil's name and personal number. It was explained to the pupils that, if they kept the certificate for five years, the fifteen shillings paid for the stamps would rise in value to one pound, which would be paid out to them at the post office. So the beach-combing expedition gave the three lads a real head start with their savings.

Other unrecognisable objects which the boys picked up on the seashore were an article made of glass, and a lead pencil which had split in the water, but which had strange words on it. The glass object had survived its sea voyage intact because it had come floating in amongst a mass of seaweed which had saved it from being smashed on the rocks. On bringing it to school, their teacher explained that it was an electric light bulb which had probably fused and was then thrown overboard from some passing ship. Very likely that would have been the first electric bulb ever to come to Portandubh, both then and for many a year afterwards.

The pencil proved to be even more interesting for the teacher told them that the words printed on it were in German, an indication that enemy vessels had been lurking in the Minch and around the west coast. She wrote the words on the blackboard – 'DEUTSCHLAND UBER ALLES' – which she translated for them as 'GERMANY OVER ALL'. This, their first introduction to a foreign language, conjured in Murdo's impressionable young mind a vision of Germany winning the war and conquering every other nation in Europe, including Britain, upon whom the wicked Huns would then inflict the atrocities which the newspapers were even now reporting, with tales of the awful deeds said to be perpetrated on the conquered Belgians. In fact, the slogan on the pencil could possibly have been given a much milder interpretation, indicating a patriotic love of the German Fatherland.

Murdo's next lesson in a foreign tongue originated very differently and in the saddest of circumstances. A public meeting had been held one evening in the school at which it was agreed that a Roll of Honour, bearing the names of all former pupils of the school who were on war service, should be hung in the classroom, and for this purpose each household in the four townships served by the school contributed money to purchase an illuminated scroll in an oaken frame, about three feet by two in dimension. The name, rank and regiment or naval vessel of each man who had gone to serve his country was entered on the scroll in Miss Mackenzie's copperplate handwriting. From time to time as the war dragged on and as more men joined up or were called up once conscription was introduced, the Roll of Honour was taken down to add more names or enter honours earned by men who had won distinction or been promoted in rank. But it was also taken down periodically for another reason, and gradually there began to appear on it, this time in red ink, the words 'pro patria'. The teacher explained to the pupils that these were Latin words meaning 'for his country', and were written against the names of men who had fallen in battle, died from wounds, or been lost at sea.

Several years later when Murdo went to High School he began to learn Latin and in one of his textbooks he came across the full quotation from which the words had been taken, in one of Horace's Odes which read, 'dulce et decorum est pro patria mori' – 'sweet and seemly it is to die for the Fatherland'.

But to these poor lads dying in long drawn-out agony amongst barbed wire entanglements and in the freezing mud of Flanders or drowning in the icy waters of the Atlantic, death must have seemed anything but sweet. And if the simple folks of Portandubh, mourning their loved ones, were to hear and understand the full words of the text, they would find it very hard to see anything seemly in their loss.

The most exciting discovery of all made by the boys, on one of their explorations along the shore, was a large metal object in the shape of a box. They had repeatedly been warned not to touch any large unfamiliar object they might come across, in case it was a mine that had broken adrift and come ashore without exploding. There had been reports of this happening at various places, although some of them had actually exploded on striking the shore. The boys could see nothing on this object resembling the 'horns' shown on warning posters distributed by the Admiralty, and which they had been told were the sensitive points of a mine, but they did not approach too close to their find, more likely from a sense of fear rather than from any thought of obedience to their parents' warning, but hurried home to report their discovery.

A coast-watching station had been established by the Admiralty at a vantage point on a headland overlooking the Minch, and it was manned by a crew of three local crofter-fishermen. It stood at a distance of about three miles from the Macleans' cottage and Mrs Maclean sent the two older boys to report the matter to the watcher in charge. He in turn reported it by telephone to his superiors at a coastguard station some thirty miles away at Broomton.

The telephone line, incidentally, was a recent innovation to the area, the first to be installed there, and specially for the use of the coast-watchers in order that they could send a quick report of any unusual or suspicious sighting to the coastguard station. The porcelain 'cups' or insulators at the tops of the poles were a sore temptation to boys and a much more interesting target for stone throwing than the usual empty cans set on fence-posts, and several of the insulators on poles that were not within sight of any houses were mysteriously broken.

But to return to the tale of the jetsam box. The following day a motorcycle and sidecar arrived carrying two men in naval uniforms. They questioned the boys who described to them exactly where the object lay, and the two men departed in the direction indicated to them. Later on, the sons of one of the coast-watchers, fellow-pupils, disclosed that their father had been informed the object was indeed a metal box, watertight, and containing the logbook of the SS *Laurentic.* This was a pre-war passenger liner which had been commandeered by the Admiralty and converted into a Red Cross hospital ship. It had been carrying wounded American soldiers home to the United States, but it was torpedoed and sunk by a German submarine in the Minch as it was heading for the Butt of Lewis. Presumably the captain's last act before the ship went down had been to consign to the sea in its watertight container the all-important logbook in the hope that it would ultimately be washed ashore and found, as indeed it was.

A tragic sequel to this occurred some time later, when two of the coast-watchers, noticing a flock of seagulls hovering over a floating object, went to investigate and found the body of a man being washed towards the shore. The body was clad only in a pyjama suit and one leg had been amputated. It was presumed that he had been one of the wounded passengers on the ill-fated vessel and he, like many others, was destined never to see his native land again. There was no identification disc or anything else that could tell anything more about him, and his mortal remains now lie in an unknown soldier's grave on the West Coast of Scotland, where the winds of the Atlantic, blowing over it from his native country in the New World, sound a coronach to mourn his passing.

As the war dragged on and the war at sea intensified with resultant great loss of shipping due to the ever-increasing attacks by German U-boats, more and more people were required not only for the fighting forces, but also for other essential war work. Women now began to volunteer in large numbers to take the place of men who were being called up from all walks of life to the fighting services. Several of the younger women of Portandubh went to work in the munition factories and in many houses only those who were too old or too young for service were left to struggle with the daily work on the crofts. Calum Maclean was over the age for fighting service, but in his younger days he had served his apprenticeship as a carpenter and he ultimately went off to Glasgow to work in one of the Clyde shipyards which were working non-stop in an endeavour to meet the ever-growing demand for replacement of the vessels lost by enemy action. By this time Sandy, the oldest of the three boys, had reached the age of fourteen, that glorious attainment for which every boy longed, so that he could leave school. Young as he was, it now became Sandy's responsibility to see to the cutting of the peats and the planting of the potatoes, so essential a supplement to their staple diet. All three boys had tried their 'prentice hand' at using the 'toruis-sgian', the peat-knife, in past summers while their father was taking a rest and smoking his pipe, so the peat-cutting was completed successfully, if rather more slowly and amateurishly. But the clumsy hand-plough, known as the 'cas-chrom', which was specially adapted for turning the ground on the sloping crofts, proved too unwieldy and heavy for Sandy's still undeveloped muscles. Gradually, however, with Sandy and James wielding ordinary garden spades, and Murdo placing the seed potatoes at ten-inch intervals along the drills, this part of the spring work was eventually completed.

Sandy's early efforts at handling the scythe to cut the hay were clumsy and ineffectual, but fortunately Calum came home in July for a week's holiday and, during that time, although the weather that summer was far from ideal, succeeded in getting the hay crop cut and the potato field hoed.

During peacetime, all supplies of food and other commodities were brought from Glasgow every ten days by a cargo vessel called *The Chieftain*, owned by a Glasgow shipping company called MacBrayne's which served all the Western Isles and all the West Coast of Scotland as far north as Lochinver. An oft-quoted piece of ribald doggerel, parodying the opening verse of the twenty-fourth psalm, said that,

> The earth belongs unto the Lord
> And all that it contains,
> Except the western Islands
> And they are all MacBraynes.

Certainly MacBraynes had the complete monopoly of all supply services to the West of Scotland, except for a very few communities in the north-west corner where an Orcadian firm had established some shops and supplied them with goods transported by a small steam vessel called *The Cormorant*. But even some of these shops also had supplies brought by MacBraynes' ship.

Normally *The Chieftain* and *The Cormorant* berthed at a pier situated about midway between the two extremities of a district that stretched for about twelve miles along the northern shore of Lochbroom, and which was served by two shops, one post office and one hotel. But shortly before the outbreak of war, the timbers of the pier were condemned as unsafe for any large vessel to moor there, so the two supply vessels had to anchor offshore as close as they could safely come to Tarbat Pier, and the two shopkeepers had to go out in rowing-boats to take their goods ashore. This was a precarious undertaking when the weather was rough with the small boats, heavily laden, pitching and tossing at the ship's side. Indeed there were occasions when it was much too stormy to risk unloading the cargo, as the laden boats were in danger of being swamped. So, under these conditions, the vessels had to steam away, leaving the community without their supplies. But fortunately these isolated townships were to a great extent self-sufficient, as far as the necessities of life were concerned.

Negotiations were being carried on to obtain Government funds for the repair of the pier, but Government red tape was just as hard to unravel and as difficult to move into action then as it is nowadays, and when war was declared all schemes of community service went into cold storage.

Not only was the area left without a serviceable pier throughout the entire duration of the war, but *The Chieftain* was commandeered by the Admiralty for war service, to be fitted out as an armed merchant cruiser, and its place was taken by a smaller vessel called *The Claymore*. The little Orcadian ship, *The Cormorant* also stopped coming as it dared not venture out into the submarine-infested waters around the Orkney Islands. Owing to wartime restrictions on the supplying of many commodities, *The Claymore* now made the trip only once a month, and when it happened that the cargo could not be unloaded because of stormy weather, the community sometimes became short of certain goods. Fortunately, these were not the essentials of life for, even in peacetime, every household kept a plentiful supply of flour and oatmeal, bought by the 'boll' which was a sack of one hundred and forty pounds. Herring caught in early autumn were salted in barrels in sufficient quantities to last throughout the winter and spring, and there were plentiful supplies of home-produced butter, cheese, eggs and home-grown potatoes. But stocks of sugar, tea and jam, all of which were rationed, sometimes ran done.

There was one occasion during the winter of nineteen sixteen, when Government warnings of the presence of enemy mines in the Minch prevented *The Claymore* from venturing to its northern ports of call for about four months. Amongst other commodities the supply of paraffin, which was the only source of lighting, ran dry. Stocks of candles, at best a very poor substitute, also went done, although occasionally a small quantity could be obtained by post from places fifty or sixty miles away that were served by rail. But then a fierce snowstorm blocked the only road into the area. Snowploughs were virtually non-existent, and certainly never appeared in outlying areas, which had to await a thaw before their roads were re-opened. For a fortnight no mail came through, nor did the townships get any war news, except for brief snippets that came by telegraph to the local post office and were passed on by word of mouth from one township to another, inevitably finishing up in great distortion, and generally with gross exaggeration.

This was a time of great delight to the schoolchildren who were, of necessity, excused from doing any home lessons because of the lack of light in their houses.

Many of the croft-houses still had their fires on open hearthstones, with no grate, all cooking being done in pots slung from a hinged iron bar built into the chimney. These houses were able to have a dim flicker of light by using the dried roots of centuries-old dead trees which were occasionally dug out of the peat-hags and which burned quite well when fully dried. When lit they were set standing in the 'ingle neuk' of the hearthstone and, as already said, gave off a dim flickering light. But the Maclean kitchen had a built-in grate without the wide gaping opening, which was a feature of hearthstone fireplaces.

When *The Claymore* eventually did arrive, there was great excitement in anticipation of getting the paraffin lamps filled up again. Practically every able-bodied person throughout the district descended on the shore opposite the anchored vessel, carrying one- and two-gallon paraffin tins, so eager were they to get a fresh supply of the much sought-after oil. Murdo, James and Sandy all were there, each with cans, for their mother, like many others, was anxious to get paraffin not only for her own use, but also for elderly neighbours who could not make the long journey to the pier.

The paraffin came in large casks, each holding around fifty gallons. As they were very bulky and heavy, and as paraffin is lighter than water, the casks were not loaded on to the boats, but were dropped into the sea, and with the use of boat-hooks were guided ashore to a shingle beach that extended eastwards from the pier.

In normal times the casks would then have been loaded on to carts and taken to the shops, to be sold there like any other commodity just when the customers required it. But, anticipating the eagerness of the community to get supplies of paraffin once more, the shopkeepers had brought along their cask spigots and their gallon measures. In no time the casks had been broached, tapped and emptied on the beach, until everyone had been supplied. The empty casks were left on the shore, to await the return of *The Claymore* for its next visit, when they would be taken back to Glasgow suppliers along with other empties – wooden crates used for commodities such as biscuits. These always came in tin boxes of dimension about fifteen inches each way, twelve of these boxes being packed in a strong wooden crate.

Butcher meat was a luxury that was seldom bought. Occasionally a crofter would kill a sheep and invariably a generous cut would be given to his neighbours. The bulk of the carcase would be cut up and salted in a barrel kept specially for the purpose. A piece would be taken out at weekends and boiled to provide not only the meat for the Sunday dinner, but also the stock for a large pan of broth, sufficient to serve the family for two days. Frequently in the Maclean household a hen that had passed its peak as a layer, or a rooster reared from the chicken broods that had been hatched out in the summer and surplus to requirements as a leader of the flock of hens, would have its neck wrung, to provide the two main courses of the Sunday dinner – a pan of barley broth, followed by the flesh of the fowl along with their own produce of potatoes and garden vegetables, and also dough-balls sweetened with syrup and sultanas and boiled in the pan of broth along with the fowl.

On all other days the main item of diet was fish, of which there was an abundant supply in the bay bordering the crofts of Portandubh. In summer there were shoals of saithe, lythe and rock-cod; it was scarcely necessary even to launch a boat for these as they could be caught from the rocks, where the water was deep enough in many places to float a large ship. In winter Murdo and his brothers dug up lugworms on the sandy beach which extended along the head of the bay. With these or with mussels and boiled limpets they baited a line which had a hundred and twenty hooks attached to it by means of short lengths of plaited horsehair spaced at intervals along the line. Now that Calum was away in Glasgow, the boys were dependent on some of the other crofters to take them out in their boats when they were going to set their own lines, but there was always someone willing to give them a place in their boat. The lines were set in zigzag fashion across the bay in the late evening with an anchor and float at each end, and they were lifted again at dawn. Although there certainly were times when they got very little return for their labours, on most occasions they were well-rewarded. These were the days before the big trawlers from Grimsby, Fleetwood and other English fishing ports had begun to plunder the sea lochs and inshore waters of Scotland's west coast. These waters were the feeding grounds of the very best of white fish and abounded in haddock, whiting, mottled cod, plaice and other fish which found a ready market and fetched high prices. But the crofters did not think of them as a saleable commodity and even if they had, there was no way in which they could get them delivered fresh to a fish market. To them, these fish were their staple diet, their staff of life, and what they did not require for their own use, they shared out liberally to families whose menfolk were away at the war, and to widows and elderly people who had no young able-bodied person to fend for them.

Chapter 14

At last the war was over. For some time now news had been trickling in of Allied forces' successes and of the collapse and submission of countries such as Turkey and Bulgaria which had entered the war on the side of the Germans. There were also rumours of unrest and uprisings by the German people against their rulers and army leaders, and there was an unconfirmed rumour that the hated Kaiser had fled to seek asylum in neutral Holland. But it was not until twenty-four hours after the 'eleventh hour of the eleventh day of the eleventh month' that the postman, hurrying for once round his delivery district, spread the glorious news, which had come to the post office by telegraph, that an armistice had been signed and hostilities had ended. There was, of course, great rejoicing on every hand, although to some the news naturally brought a fresh awakening of sorrow and grief at the thought that for them there would be no husband, son or sweetheart returning with the triumphant band of servicemen soon to be demobilised.

Demobilisation of course did not occur immediately or *en bloc*. First of all the women who had gone to the munition factories came home, followed by the younger girls who had enlisted to serve as auxiliary nurses with the Red Cross. Gradually small groups of men returned, some of them limping, or with their arms in slings; for the wounded who had been in hospital when the fighting ceased were released as soon as they were able to travel.

But at last all who were still alive of the men who had so proudly marched away four years earlier, or who had enlisted or been called up at a later date, were back home.

How different their returning was from what their friends at home had anticipated. For them there was no great rejoicing, but rather a complete disillusionment of the ideas which had been instilled into them by politicians, and by their officers too, about the splendour and nobleness of war. They had experienced nothing that was splendid or noble in floundering through freezing trenches, running deep in Flanders mud. Barbed wire entanglements that were supposed to be their protection against an attacking enemy too often proved to be really a death-trap where so many of their wounded comrades had died in agony before help could be brought to them. At first they felt that they could find some comfort in the belief that they had fought 'a war to end all wars' and that they had helped to preserve 'a land fit for heroes to dwell in' – a high-sounding phrase so often uttered by the politicians who had sent them to war. How tragically soon they were to be disillusioned about that also!

While the Government showered titles and other honours on men who had stayed safely at home, amassing huge fortunes in the turning out of weapons of war at grossly inflated prices, too often ignoring the basic regulations that were required to ensure the efficiency of the weapons produced, the men who had risked life and limb in the operating of these weapons were now neglected and forgotten. Where now was the 'land fit for heroes to dwell in'? Throughout the whole country returning soldiers and sailors were to find that there was no work for them. Their jobs had either folded up or had been filled by others, and the government that had made such fulsome promises when calling them up to fight, now made no effort to provide alternative employment. In fact shipyards and factories now began to pay off large numbers of their workforce. For those who did retain jobs, wages began to fall while prices of goods in the shops still remained as high as ever, and poverty and hunger began to rear their ugly heads throughout the industrial cities and towns.

In Portandubh as in other Highland communities, the returning ex-servicemen at least had their crofts to work on, with their boats and fishing gear to augment their livelihood, so they would not starve. But after four years of service overseas, many of them now became restless of the simple country life with which they had been contented in pre-war days, and as there was little hope of employment for them in industrial Britain, they now began to look towards the British Colonies where there were prospects of employment for them in the agricultural development of these lands, which was the type of work that they knew. So once more, the young men of Portandubh, and some of the young women also, began to leave their homes and emigrate.

About eighteen months after the end of the war, Calum Maclean was paid off from the shipyard in Glasgow where he had been employed, and as there was no hope of getting work at any of the other yards, which were all running their workforces down, he returned home. His coming now released Sandy from the responsibilities of the croft, and he began to look around for paid employment.

The minister of the district, whose manse and church were in Polbuie, had a glebe extending to about four acres of arable land as well as some rough grazing. He had a very large family, so he found it expedient and even necessary not to depend on the generosity of his congregation, lavish as that was, and he decided to keep a couple of milking cows and to cultivate the arable part of the glebe. But the demands of his time as pastor of a flock scattered over a very wide area did not leave him with adequate time for pastoral efforts in agriculture, so young Sandy was engaged to be the 'minister's man'. As the manse was about five miles distant from the Maclean's cottage, he got both board and accommodation at the manse, there being one wing of the building that was purpose-built for the housing of servants, although, in this case, Sandy was the only employee of the manse, the minister's wife and the two older girls having to cope with the domestic chores.

Sandy's departure split up the young Macleans' triumvirate. But, in any case, the boys were now reaching an age when their boyish ploys might be considered by their school playmates to be too childish. They also had to give more time to the work that devolved upon them assisting their father on the croft, owing to Sandy's departure.

But for Murdo and James there now developed a new interest of which they took full advantage when it was their turn to go to the shop for the rations, a word which incidentally was pronounced 'rayshuns' by everybody in the locality. This pronunciation was arrived at quite logically by analogy, comparing it with the word 'nations'.

Although this was fully eighteen months after the end of the war, so much of the country's shipping had been sunk that certain commodities were still in short supply and were still strictly rationed.

When the boys had completed their purchases at the shop, they now made a point of calling at the manse, ostensibly to visit their brother, but actually to develop a friendship with the children of the manse, the five oldest of whom were quite close to each other in age, and two of whom had the same ages as James and Murdo.

A burn, which at one time had driven a mill-wheel nearby, ran through the manse glebe and it was a favourite sport of the children to go paddling in this burn, splashing about and poking under the banks to try and dislodge any small trout that might be hiding there. The burn was not big enough to harbour fish of a usable size, but chasing them provided the youngsters with good sport even although the trout were too nimble to be caught by hand.

On one occasion, when it was Murdo's turn to do the shopping, he paid his usual dutiful visit to brother Sandy, and then, depositing his pillowslip of groceries beside the wall which surrounded the glebe, he went to join the manse children at their play. An hour passed very quickly and when the minister's wife came to call her family in, it was time for Murdo to set off on his journey home. But when he went to collect his homely shopping-bag, he found to his dismay that one of the minister's cows, which he had not noticed grazing nearby, when he laid his bag of groceries down, had got there before him, and had obviously looked upon Murdo's bag as a treat specially set there for her. The loaf of bread had been devoured, the packet of margarine had also vanished, undoubtedly going the same road as the loaf, and the bag of sugar had burst and was scattered beyond any hope of recovery. Only the tea and the bacon were in a fit state to be considered still usable. The culprit was now contentedly chewing the pillowslip, half of which still dangled out of her slavering mouth. It was with the greatest reluctance that she finally yielded up the tattered remnants of the pillowslip to Sandy, who had to pull with all his strength to get it away, as he feared that the cow might choke on it. It was, of course, now only fit to be consigned to the rubbish bin.

Murdo was in utter dismay at the thought of having to go home with nothing except the miserable remnants of shopping which had escaped the cow's attention, but the kindly lady of the manse consoled him to some degree by replacing the pillowslip and also a portion of the goods which had vanished into the cow's stomach, probably the first thing she had ever eaten over which she would not have to ruminate. During all of his five-mile journey home, poor Murdo had to ruminate in quite a different way over how he was to explain away his loss to his parents. The humour of the situation, however, plus the lugubrious expression on Murdo's face as he stammered out his tale of woe, must have outweighed any annoyance which his mother must have felt at the loss of two precious pounds of rationed sugar, for nothing very severe was said to him, beyond an admonition to be sure in future to 'keep his bags below his eyes'.

But time was now running short for Murdo's carefree life of boyhood pastimes. Shortly before the school closed for the summer vacation, the teacher got the usual annual intimation that any promising pupils who wished to enter a bursary competition with a view to continuing in school for secondary education should go to Polbuie school on a certain date, where a test would be set to them under supervision. Murdo certainly had no desire to continue at school after the age of fourteen, but his parents and his teacher had other ideas. Miss Mackenzie interviewed his father and mother and, with their wholehearted agreement, Murdo and another boy who was considered a potential candidate for secondary education, set out early one Saturday morning to walk the six-mile distance to Polbuie school, in time to arrive there for ten o'clock where they met six other boys and girls who had assembled from Polbuie and another neighbouring school.

The local minister, who was supervising the examination, first allocated to them seats that were well-spaced apart. He then handed out sheets of foolscap paper and told them to write their name, age and school at the head of the sheet, after which he spoke a gentle word of warning about the dire result which would follow any detected collusion during the course of the examination. Then, on the stroke of ten o'clock, a printed test paper was handed out and heads and hands went quickly to work.

First there was an arithmetic test with six questions, three being straight calculations, and the other three problems which had to be solved by logical reasoning. At the end of one hour exactly the arithmetic papers were gathered in and an English test paper distributed along with a fresh supply of foolscap paper. The English paper was a test in grammar, syntax and the writing of an essay, which had to be at least one foolscap page in length, selecting a subject from three prescribed titles. The time allowed for this test was one and a half hours, and sharp on the stroke of twelve-thirty, the contestants were told to stop writing and the papers were collected. Outside there was some animated discussion amongst the participants as they compared notes to see if they had got the correct answers to the arithmetic questions, after which they departed their several ways.

Some weeks later, intimation came to the school that Murdo had won a bursary which amounted to the princely sum of twelve pounds per annum, payable in three instalments at the end of each term.

The nearest secondary school was at Broomton, a fishing village about twenty-five miles from Portandubh. Obviously Murdo would not be able to get home except during school holidays, so it became necessary for Murdo and his mother to make an advance visit to Broomton, travelling on the mail car, which, in itself, was a new experience for Murdo, who had never sat in a motorcar before. The purpose of the trip was first to find suitable lodgings, and then to visit the shops in order to fit Murdo out with a new suit of clothes and a new pair of shoes. For, most certainly, there would be no barefooted pupils at Broomton school.

For Murdo this was the end of an era.